GAL...

BE YOUR OWN DOCTOR USING

REIKI

by

Dr. Dhiren Gala

B.Sc., D.H.M.S., D.O., D.Ac.,
C.G.O., C.C.H., A.R.S.H.

With

Dr. D. R. Gala

N.D., D.N.O., D.C.O.

Dr. Sanjay Gala

M.B. (BOM.), M.S. (ENT)

NAVNEET®

NAVNEET PUBLICATIONS (INDIA) LIMITED

Navneet House	Navneet Bhavan
Gurukul Road, Memnagar, Ahmadabad – 380 052. Phone : 5530 5000	Bhavani Shankar Road, Dadar, Mumbai – 400 028. Phone : 5662 6565

DHANLAL BROTHERS DISTRIBUTORS

70, Princess Street, Mumbai – 400 002.
Phone : 2201 7027

Visit us at : www.navneet.com & connectschool.com   G 4523

e-mail : npil@navneet.com

Price : Rs. 25.00

For 1st, 2nd & 3rd degree attunements and Reiki seminars, contact:

Dr. Dhiren Gala

1st Floor, Abbas Building 'A',
Near Tilak Market, Jalbhai Lane,
Harkisondas Hospital Road, Mumbai – 400 004.
Phone : 2386 7275

NAVNEET PUBLICATIONS (INDIA) LIMITED

Mumbai : 1. Bhavani Shankar Road, Dadar, **Mumbai – 400 028.**
(Tel. 5662 6565 • Fax : 5662 6470)

2. **Navyug Distributors :** Road No. 8, M. I. D. C., Next to Indian Institute of Packaging, Marol, Andheri (East), **Mumbai – 400 093.** (Tel. 2821 4186 • Fax : 2835 2758)

Ahmadabad : Navneet House, Gurukul Road, Memnagar, **Ahmadabad – 380 052.**
(Tel. 5530 5000)

Bangalore : Sri Balaji's, No. 12, 2nd Floor, 3rd Cross, Malleswaram, **Bangalore – 560 003.**
(Tel. 2346 5740)

Bhopal : Navneet Sadan, E-7/728, Arera Colony, Shahpura, **Bhopal – 462 016.** (Tel. 527 8544)

Chennai : 30, Sriram Nagar, North Street, Alwarpet, **Chennai – 600 018.** (Tel. 2434 6404)

Delhi : 2-E/23, Orion Plaza, 2nd & 3rd Floor, Jhandewalan Extn., **New Delhi – 110 055.**
(Tel. 2361 0170)

Hyderabad : Bldg. No. 3-2-331, 2nd Floor, Somasundaram Street, **Secunderabad – 500 025.**
(Tel. 5531 7348)

Kolkata : Newar Bhavan, 1st Floor, No. 87, Chowringhee Road, **Kolkata – 700 020.**
(Tel. 2223 2497)

Nagpur : 63, Opp. Shivaji Science College, Congress Nagar, **Nagpur – 440 012.** (Tel. 252 1522)

Nashik : Dharmaraj Plaza, Old Gangapur Naka, Gangapur Road, **Nashik – 422 005.**
(Tel. 231 0627)

Navsari : 3/C, Arvind Nagar Society, Lunsikui Road, **Navsari – 396 445.** (Tel. 244 186)

Patna : 1st Floor, 36-D, Sahdeo Mahto Marg, Srikrishnapuri, **Patna – 800 001.** (Tel. 220 4921)

Pune : Sita Park, 18, Shivaji Nagar, Near Bharat English School, **Pune – 411 005.** (Tel. 2553 6364)

Surat : 1, Ground Floor, Sri Vallabh Complex, Kotwal Street, Nanpara, **Surat – 395 001.**
(Tel. 246 3927)

Vadodara : F-1, Vaidya Vatika, Opp. Hanuman Wadi, Sardar Bhuvan Khancho,
Vadodara – 390 001.

PREFACE

It can no longer be denied that it is impossible to wipe out diseases merely by medication. It also cannot be denied that we need to pay greater attention to the prevention of diseases rather than their treatment. People need to be educated and encouraged to take an active interest in their own health. They should be trained in non-medical therapeutic systems which are effective as well as safe. Reiki therapy is one such system and, of late, has generated a lot of interest in the public. To cater to this curiosity, a number of books on Reiki therapy have been brought out.

As we read these books, we realise that somewhere along the line, this essentially simple therapy has been converted into, and projected as, a complex system requiring a lot of mind-control, concentration and meditation. Moreover, its reputation has been tainted with mistruths and unreasonable claims of efficacy. This, of course, is a matter of great concern.

We, therefore, feel that the time has come to establish the basic tenets of Reiki therapy. We have presented in this book the essence of Reiki therapy in a scientific, yet intelligible manner. Moreover, going against common practice, we have refrained from stocking the book with personal anecdotes and numerous accounts of miraculous case histories, that do nothing but impose pressure upon the reader's sense of logic.

This book would not have seen the light of the day without the selfless help of a number of persons : my dear friend Jitendra Rana, who painstakingly researched the subject; Dr Rekha Rupani, Dr Nilesh Thaker, Dr Subhash Gokhale, Dr Jayesh Shah, Dr Manjushree Sengupta and Dr Kalpana Desai (Chandgadkar) who perused the manuscript and offered valuable suggestions; last but not the least, my family members who allowed me to spend on this book, such time of mine that was otherwise rightfully theirs.

Suggestions for the improvement of this book are solicited and shall be positively considered at the time of bringing out future editions.

– **Author**

CONTENTS

NOTE

Only the male gender has been used throughout this book. This has been done to make the reading simpler and not with any ulterior motive.

1. INTRODUCTION

An irregular, reckless life-style and faulty dietary habits have wrought havoc with the health and the lives of people. Constitutional diseases like diabetes, high blood pressure, coronary heart disease, asthma, arthritis, etc. are steadily on the rise. To help the ailing humanity, a number of treatment methods, medicinal as well as non-medicinal, have come into existence. Medical forms of treatment are, undeniably, more popular. The reasons for such a state of affairs are not far to seek. For a doctor, practising medicine is an easy, time-effective and profitable venture. A doctor in general-practice can examine and treat more than a hundred patients a day. On the other hand, practising non-medicinal therapies requires a lot of time and labour, which is out of step with the socio-economic determinants of modern age. Even the patients, today, have become easy-going. Rather than taking active interest in their health-matters, they want to sit back and let the doctors fix them up!

However, the drawbacks of medicinal treatments are gradually coming to light. In general, most medicinal therapies try merely to relieve symptoms rather than striking at the root-cause of disease (i.e., imbalance of body-energy). Such symptomatic treatment merely suppresses the disease, which is bound to resurface later. Secondly, medicines produce undesirable (and sometimes fatal) side-effects. Thirdly, with the advent of super-specialist doctors, five star hospitals and high tech instruments, medical treatment is becoming more and more expensive. All of us have seen many families brought to ruin by enormous medical expenses. Finally, medical sciences are, increasingly, becoming impersonal and technical, the clinician being more interested in the disease than the patient. Dr Francis Peabody wrote in the Journal of American Medical Association : 'One of the essential qualities of a clinician is genuine interest in humanity, for the care of the patient involves caring for the patient'. However, not many doctors pay heed to this advice.

A growing awareness about the shortcomings of medicines has made people seek alternative forms of treatment which use one or the other form of healing energy rather than chemical medicines. To such people, Reiki therapy offers itself as an excellent alternative.

Reiki (pronounced Ray-key) is a Japanese word formed by two terms : Rei, which means universal and ki, which means life force or energy. Reiki is the healing energy which is abundantly present in the universe. In Reiki therapy, this energy is utilised to boost the body-energy and the immunity. Thereby, health can be maintained and disease can be alleviated or cured. Of the numerous energy therapies presently in use (viz. Reiki, Acupuncture, Pranic healing, Spiritual healing, Radionics, Bio-energetics, etc.), Reiki therapy is the simplest. Its use can be learnt by one and all, even by those who have no previous scientific or medical knowledge. While treating, the healer merely has to place his hands on the patient or his diseased body-part. No active effort (manipulation) or concentration is required on his part. The moment he places his palms on the patient and invokes Reiki, it flows into his own body and then emerges out of his hands to enter the patient's body. This flow continues on its own till the needs of the patient (for that moment) have been satisfied. The healer merely acts as a channel or a connecting link between the universal energy (i.e., Reiki) and the patient's energy. Unlike other forms of energy medicine, Reiki therapy does not involve diagnosing an imbalance in the patient's energy-field or intentionally repatterning it. The healer has very little power over the direction, the intensity or the amount of Reiki flowing into the patient's body; these are determined by Reiki itself, which is infinitely intelligent. In Reiki therapy, therefore, there is no scope for mistakes, failure or misuse.

Reiki therapy enjoys a number of other advantages, too. Apart from having a curative aspect, it also has a preventive aspect. A healthy person who receives Reiki regularly can easily avert illness. That is precisely why a Reiki therapist is able to maintain perfect health; Reiki has to pass through his body first, before being transmitted to the patient. Agitated and saddened by the state of conventional therapeutics, philosophers have remarked, 'Physician, heal thyself'. While healing patients, a Reiki therapist actually heals himself, too. And since he is not using his own energy for healing, he never feels depleted or exhausted.

Reiki therapy can be effectively combined with other forms of treatment, including medicine. It is for this reason that Reiki therapy is finding favour with more and more medical doctors. Doctors find that when they add Reiki to their arsenal, their patients recover in less time than expected.

Reiki therapy is an excellent form of psycho-therapy. It brings about profound, positive changes in the recipient's mind. He becomes relaxed, calm and composed. He becomes capable of handling stress quite easily, as things and situations are understood more clearly. In fact, his whole attitude to life changes, for the better. His imaginative and creative powers increase. Some advanced practitioners of Reiki have even reported development of extra-sensory powers.

Medical therapies look at disease as a physical entity that invades the victim's body and needs to be attacked and conquered. Exponents of energy-medicine, on the other hand, say that diseases are caused by a derangement of bodily energy. A disease first begins at the energy level. Much later (sometimes after months) does it manifest at the physical level. In other words, physical disease is secondary to energy imbalance. In support of their claim they cite a simple experiment :

(1) Using a Kirlian camera, photograph a leaf attached to a branch of a living plant. Its energy-field (aura) can be clearly visualised.

(2) Cut the leaf off the branch and throw it away.

(3) Photograph the plant again. The energy-field of the leaf is seen to persist.

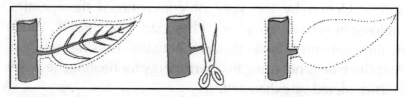

This goes to prove that the energy-body is a template which moulds the physical body. In other words, energy-body is the 'cause' and physical body merely its 'effect'. Treatment directed at the physical body alone is likely to act only palliatively. Reiki itself being an energy, interacts with, and restores a state of balance to, the bodily energy. It, thus, strikes at the fundamental or root cause of disease and acts curatively.

In summary, we would say that Reiki therapy is an energy therapy par excellence. It realigns, recharges and rebalances the body-energy. Acting through the autonomous nervous system and the endocrine system, it restores homoeostasis and enhances immunity. It is not a placebo or a form of auto-suggestion as some doctors would have people to believe. It helps independently of belief system, emotional state or religious preference. It works on insane or unconscious persons, young children, animals and even plants. Indeed, it is a God-given or Nature-given gift to mankind.

A question that is sure to arise in the reader's mind is that, 'If Reiki is so good, if it is all-pervading and omni-present, if it is a God-intended gift, why is it not naturally available to each of us? Why are human-beings not born with an innate ability to tap it from the space?

To understand the answer to this question, we will have to first understand the dynamics of bio-energy 'Prana'.

Prana possesses a form or a structure of its own called the bio-plasmic or energy body, which not only inhabits our physical body but also extends out of the body forming the 'aura'. In other words, aura is the external manifestation of our energy-body.

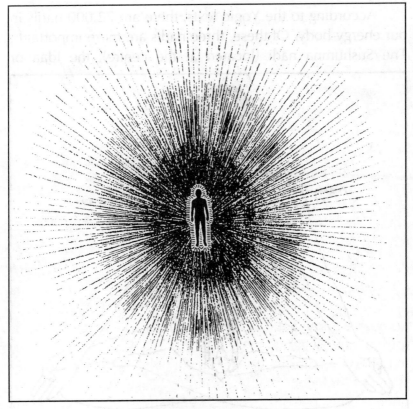

Fig. 1.1 : The human aura

This aura can be visualised on a Kirlian photograph and gives reliable information about the person's health. In good health, the aura is quite uniform and extensive. A shrunken aura signifies low vitality whereas an uneven aura is a sign of existing (or future) illness. The energy-body and the physical body are inter-dependent, one affecting the other.

The energy-body contains energy channels (called nadis or meridians) and energy centres (called chakras). A lot has been written about nadis and chakras in Vedas, the ancient Indian text-books of medicine and yoga; we will present only the essence over here.

According to the Yogic texts, there are 72,000 nadis in our energy-body. Of these, three nadis are more important : The Sushumna nadi (located at the centre), the Idaa or

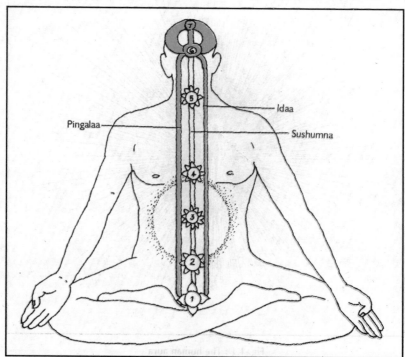

Fig. 1.2 : The major nadis

Chandra nadi (located to the left of Sushumna nadi) and the Pingalaa or Surya nadi (located to the right of Sushumna nadi). Nadis ensure a circulation of bio-energy 'Prana' throughout the body. Nadis being energy entities are not visible to the naked eye. Their physical counterparts are the spinal cord and the paraspinous chains of nerve-ganglia.

According to the Yogic texts, there are 48 perpetually spinning chakras (wheels or centres of energy) in our

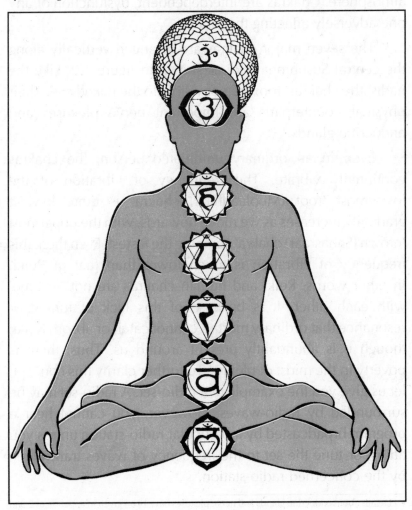

Fig. 1.3 : The major chakras (front view)

energy-body. Of these, seven are major chakras, 21 are minor chakras and 20 are mini chakras. Chakras are a link between the bio-energy Prana and atmospheric energies. Each chakra is associated with a specific region or a system of the body, as elaborated in appendix 2, either supplying or draining energy. Depending upon the need of a body-region, the associated chakra absorbs energy from (or emits energy to) the atmosphere. Chakras are interdependent, dysfunction of any one adversely affecting the others.

The seven major chakras are arranged vertically along the central Sushumna nadi as shown in figure 1.2. Like the nadis, the chakras, too, are not visible to the naked eye. Their physical counterparts are important nerve plexuses and endocrine glands.*

Even in an ordinary uninitiated person, the chakras continually vibrate. The frequency of vibration of the lowermost 'root (Moolaadhaar) chakra' is quite low. It gradually increases as we move upwards, with the uppermost 'crown (Sahasraar) chakra' spinning the fastest. Even then, this frequency of vibration is much lower than that of Reiki. In other words, Reiki and human chakras are not 'in tune' with each other. It is because of this lack of tuning or resonance that ordinary mortals cannot catch or absorb Reiki, though it is abundantly present around us. Thus, there is poverty in the midst of plenty! To further clarify this concept, let us give you the example of a radio-set. A radio-set may be surrounded by radio-waves. However, you cannot hear a program broadcasted by a particular radio-station unless you adjust or tune the set to the frequency of waves transmitted by the concerned radio-station.

---

* Details about endocrine glands and nerve plexuses have been given in appendices 2 and 3 at the end of this book.

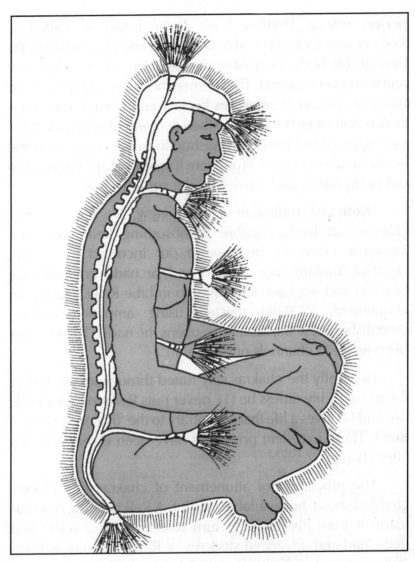

Fig. 1.4 : The major chakras (side view)

For a person to be able to absorb Reiki, it is necessary that the vibratory frequency of his chakras be drastically raised. This is done by a trained Reiki master, through a short, confidential procedure known as 'attunement or initiation'. This charging of chakras is the very essence of Reiki therapy and sets it apart from other energy therapies. The fortunate person whose chakras have been tuned is called a Reiki-channel, i.e., he is able to receive and channelize Reiki through his body for treating himself and others, whenever and wherever required. The moment he invokes Reiki with an intention to heal, it enters his body from the top through the crown (Sahasraar) chakra and then descends through the third eye (Aagyaa) and the throat (Vishuddha) chakras to reach the heart (Anaahat) chakra. From here it enters his arms to emerge out of his hands and move into the patient's body.

(**Note :** According to another view, we are all Reiki channels at birth, capable of absorbing Reiki from the Universe. However, because of our incorrect living and negative thinking, our chakras and/or nadis gradually get blocked and we lose our ability to imbibe Reiki. During an attunement, a Reiki master, using amplified energy, demolishes these blocks and re-opens the nadis. Thereby, we become Reiki channels once again.)

Generally the chakras stay tuned throughout the rest of the person's life unless he (1) never puts Reiki to therapeutic use and (2) lives a life that is contrary to the 'five principles' of Reiki. These excellent principles have been elaborated in a later chapter.

The procedure of attunement of chakras is a closely guarded secret, not available in print. A Reiki master, who has learnt it from his peers, in turn teaches it to a select few dedicated and advanced students of Reiki, converting them into masters.

While such secrecy might be necessary to preserve the sanctity of Reiki and prevent its misuse, it has resulted into people associating Reiki therapy with hypnotism or even black-magic. However, we want to assure the reader and the world that this is not the case. The process of attunement barely takes ten minutes. While the master is performing the ritual on a subject (i.e., charging his chakras), the latter remains fully conscious and calm. In fact, at the end of the process, he feels invigorated and rejuvenated. Indeed, he has been converted from an ordinary mortal into a Reiki channel, ready to take on the world of sickness.

We will reiterate that the training in the actual process of attunement of chakras is imparted to a chosen few, in an orthodox 'guru-shishya' tradition. 'Who started this tradition and when?' you may rightly ask. The story goes back to the late eighteenth century when Dr Mikaomi Usui, a Japanese monk, rediscovered Reiki. This history of Reiki has been presented in the next chapter.

2. HISTORY

The history of Reiki is as old as the history of the universe. But in its current form, it was rediscovered by Dr Mikaomi Usui of Japan, about a hundred years ago. While the exact details of the story are shrouded in mystery, we will present the essence over here.

Fig. 2.1 : Dr Mikaomi Usui

Born on the 15th August, 1862, Dr Mikaomi Usui was a preacher who spoke highly of the lives and the work of Lord Buddha and Lord Jesus. Once he remarked about their fantastic abilities to heal the sick and revive even the dead. The students asked him if he really believed in what he said and, if so, knew the procedure of healing. Dr Usui was unable to give a convincing answer and, in a true Japanese tradition of humility, resigned his post as a preacher. There-after began his long quest for the answer, which took him to a number of countries and inspired him to learn numerous languages, including Sanskrit. However, no satisfactory information was coming forth. Dejected, Dr Usui returned to his homeland Japan. He, now, decided to conduct inquiries with Buddhist monks. He soon realised that none of them was keen to discuss the subject of physical healing. Being religiously evolved souls, they were more concerned with the healing of the spirit rather than the healing of the body. Physical sufferings were desirable compensatory phenomena, they believed, which enabled the person to wash off the debts of karma. Dr Usui realised that Reiki therapy, once very well known and in common use, had been lost to the world for the sole reason that the sages and the elite had simply disregarded physical healing which, they thought, was superfluous. Nonetheless, he decided to continue his search which, ultimately, led him to a Buddhist monastery. The old priest of this monastery was not averse to the idea of physical healing, perhaps due to the fact that he was himself bed-ridden from agonising pain of arthritis. "If Lord Buddha did it, why should we look down upon it?", he opined. He encouraged Dr Usui to study the holy books that were gathering dust in the monastery. The task was arduous but Dr Usui was determined to see the light. His labour was finally rewarded when he came across Sanskrit sutras (verses) that revealed the formulae, the symbols and the steps to effect healing. The sutras also said that it was necessary to establish contact with a (undescribed) higher power to be able to put the formulae to actual use. Thus, the intellectual answer to the problem of healing had been found; what was now lacking was 'empowerment'. Since the old priest was of no further help, Dr Usui decided to pray and meditate for further guidance. He went to a nearby sacred hill called Mt. Kurama and began with meditation and fasting. For a full twenty days, nothing seemed to happen. On the early morning of the twenty-first day, Dr Usui had an incredible experience. While in a state of deep meditative trance, he visualised a beam of bright **light** approaching him, entering his head and spreading into his whole body. Millions of rainbow coloured bubbles and, finally, three-dimensional symbols appeared before his mind's eyes. He also received information about the precise method of employing the symbols to activate the healing energy. Thus, Dr Usui had been converted into an **'enlightened'** being in a literal sense. Indeed, it was the first modern-day 'attunement', the psychic rediscovery of an ancient method of healing.

Dr Usui left Mt. Kurama, having realised how to heal as Buddha and Jesus had done. Climbing down the mountain, he experienced what are traditionally known as four miracles. First : he stubbed his toe, which healed as he put his hand instinctively on it. Second : he stuffed his stomach with food, forgetting that he had not consumed anything but water for twenty-one days. The heaviness in his stomach vanished as he put his hands on it. Third : he healed the toothache of the woman who had served him the meal. Fourth : on his return to the monastery, he treated and cured the old priest of his arthritis.

Dr Usui named the healing energy 'Reiki', which means universal life-force or energy and set about the task of healing the sick in right earnest. He toured the length and breadth of

Japan, not only healing people but also teaching Reiki therapy to the desirous. He created three degrees for the training in Reiki therapy which he named shoden (first teaching), okuden (inner teaching) and shinpickden (mystery teaching). Dr Usui is thought to have 'initiated' about 2000 people in Reiki therapy, one of which was Dr Chujiro Hayashi. Dr Hayashi took Reiki therapy out of Japan, to the West. From there, it spread (and is still spreading) to the rest of the world.

It is necessary to present over here, an experience of Dr Usui, which is both interesting and instructive. Once, he was drawn to a beggars' colony, thronged by scores of debilitated and handicapped people. Driven by compassion, Dr Usui decided to free them of their illnesses free of charge, so that they could start a new life. However, he was 'in' for a shock. He saw the same faces returning to him time and again. He saw them still begging instead of making an honest living. Disillusioned and disappointed, he bade good-bye to the slums.

Dr Usui's experience in the slums is used by some unscrupulous, material-minded practitioner-teachers to justify the high price of Reiki-training and Reiki therapy today, the premise being that a person who does not pay for something is unlikely to appreciate its true worth (or the more dearly a person is made to pay for something, the more he will value it). They have coined the phrase 'exchange of energy' for the transaction (i.e., they demand monetary energy in exchange for the universal energy). We believe it is immoral to drag Dr Usui's name in this controversy. Every doctor, every therapist has a family to support and a clinic to maintain. If he honestly and plainly says that he is charging (like any other doctor) for the health-services he is rendering or for the time he is devoting (towards Reiki-training or Reiki therapy), no one with even a semblance of reasoning power will object to it. In fact, Reiki is invaluable. Charging a sky-high fee for Reiki-training or Reiki therapy and calling it an exchange of energy will still amount to devaluation of Reiki.

We believe that Dr Usui's disappointment was due, not to the fact that beggars did not pay, but to the fact that he had healed only their bodies, not their minds and spirits. On retrospection, Dr Usui himself realised his folly of concentrating only on physical healing, disregarding the Buddhist ideal of spiritual healing. It was then, that he understood why almost all Buddhist sages he had approached prior to his enlightenment, had discouraged him from persuing the subject of bodily healing. He immediately felt compelled to incorporate certain spiritual principles in all teaching/healing he undertook. A student/patient was accepted for training/treatment only if he promised to live a life that conformed to these principles.

These principles, five in number, make Reiki therapy a complete therapy which heals not only the body but also the spirit. These excellent principles have been enlisted in the next chapter.

3. THE FIVE PRINCIPLES

Just for today I will not worry.

Just for today I will not get angry.

Just for today I will be honest.

Just for today I will count my blessings.

Just for today I will give love and show respect to every living being.

Each day is a lifetime in miniature!

To awaken each morning is to be born again,
to fall asleep at night is to die to the day.

In between waking and sleeping are
the golden hours of the day.

What we think we **cannot** do for a lifetime,
we **can** do for a daytime.

Anyone can strive to be happy for a day
and to spread happiness around.

Anyone can rise above fear for a day
and meet each situation with courage.

Anyone can hold his temper for a day
and guard the words he speaks.

Anyone can remain honest for a day
and carry his burden heroically.

Anyone can count his blessings for a day
deciding, not to look at half-empty but at half-filled glass.

Anyone can eschew hate and cruelty for a day
deciding to live and let live.

Live a day at a time and remember that
tomorrow is another today!

4. THE FIRST DEGREE TRAINING

The first degree seminar is a very important and auspicious event in a person's life wherein he is transformed from an ordinary mortal into a 'Reiki channel', ready to take on the world of illness : physical as well as mental. He can, thereafter, treat not only himself but also others through simple laying-on of his hands.

The first degree seminar essentially brings about an attunement of the participant's chakras (energy centres) to Reiki, through an ancient technological process which, though simple and short, is very powerful.

When people come to register for the seminar, they often ask as to whether it is necessary for them to prepare beforehand for the seminar by browsing through a book on Reiki, by performing specific exercises, by resorting to fasting or meditation, by abstaining from intoxicants or sex, and so forth.

A little preparation before undertaking the seminar, though not indispensable, is desirable. Such a preparation creates a platform for the participant, from which he can take a quantum leap (towards the goal of physical and mental well-being) with the help of an attunement.

In the days before the seminar, spare some time for yourself on a regular basis and make it clear to yourself what you expect from your life. Do you desire more love and fulfillment in your relationships? Are you looking for a better job? Do you wish to solve a health-problem? Whatever it may be, the attunement can trigger off a positive development in every matter important to you. It can accelerate the learning and evolutionary processes within you, thereby contributing to a happier and healthier life.

Don't plan or undertake strenuous activities just prior to or during the seminar. Avoid junk food, non-vegetarian foods and alcohol for at least a week before the scheduled day of the seminar. During that period, perform deep breathing exercise for about five minutes, once or twice a day. **Not that attunements will not take effect if you disregard this advice; they will still act equally well.** But if your body or your mind is under stress, you will not be able to perceive the subtle changes taking place within you.

On the morning of the seminar-day, take a thorough bath with tepid water. Dress yourself with comfortable, loose-fitting, clean clothes, but avoid all jewellery. Keep back your pagers and cell-phones at home.

The seminar is designed differently by each Reiki master. Although certain components such as the four initiations, the telling of the Reiki story and the instructions for treating the self and others are always the same, everything else is planned in accordance with the personality and interests of the concerned master.

This type of seminar design contributes to keeping the course lively and exciting. Rigid concepts hinder the spontaneity of the seminar leader and that of the participants as well. The seminars held by the same master often vary from each other in their structure. The world is constantly changing; so are we and our interests. Responding to this liveliness very well suits the quality of Reiki which does have an individual effect.

The seminar is conducted at a quiet place, having peaceful, natural surroundings. The relaxed atmosphere of the room befits the auspicious occasion. The air is filled with fragrance of fresh flowers or incense sticks. As participants come in, their ears are greeted by notes of soft, devotional music and their eyes are brightened by burning camphor or candles. These purify the atmosphere and keep the seminar room free from negative energies. The entrants can, indeed, sense the positive vibrations which fill the room.

The course begins in the seminar-hall after all the participants (about ten to twenty) have assembled. The Reiki master introduces himself. Each participant is then asked to introduce himself as regards his name, occupation and the reason for joining the seminar. While a few have come out of simple curiosity, most others have come because they have seen or felt 'Reiki-miracles', and they now want to experience the power of Reiki in their own hands. Many participants are spouses or friends of people who have already taken the first degree some time ago. They have seen their near ones change almost overnight following attunement. They have seen them becoming more loving, open-minded and lively. Some people come because they believe that the attunement will be a big step forward on their spiritual path. Many participants confess to having personal difficulties in emotional or physical area; they would like to do something for their health on their own, take personal responsibility and protect themselves from future serious illnesses. Medical doctors, too, enroll for the seminar, having received the tip from a professional colleague. Despite the strong recommendations, they are skeptical : "It just can't be that easy; there must be a catch somewhere!" They come hoping against hope that the strange business will turn out to be worthwhile.

After the participants have come to know each other, the teacher introduces the concept of Reiki. He gives details of what it is and what it is not; what it can do and what it cannot. He informs that Reiki being an energy interacts with human chakras, which in turn affect the physical body. He gives complete details about chakras as regards their locations and body-parts/system each of them controls. (This information has been tabulated in appendix 2.) He then breaks the gladdening news that the chakras of each participant will be 'attuned' so as to render them capable of absorbing Reiki. This is akin to upgarding a T.V. set; previously it could capture signals sent by a few stations but now it can capture signals broadcasted by many stations.

Next comes a brief account of Reiki-history : its origin, its rediscovery by Dr. Mikaomi Usui and its subsequent spread to the nooks and corners of the world.

The participants are, then, given the information, charts and demonstrations about the places (body-parts) where hands are to be placed while treating oneself or others. Details of these basic hand-positions and their sequential order are presented in the next chapter.

The participants are informed that the attunement is to follow shortly, but before that they should start placing their hands for about three minutes on each of the body-parts (in the suggested order) so as to possibly feel a subtle flow of energy through their plams into their bodies. This is the person's own bio-energy which is quite weak as compared to Reiki which is immensely powerful. Any person who places his plams on a body-part before the attunement and immediately after the attunement is amazed to feel the enormous difference in the energy-flow.

While the participants are busy learning the basic hand-positions, the attunements begin in a separate 'attunement room'. While most Reiki masters prefer to attune one participant at a time, there are some who invite three to five participants into the room. On an average, it takes about three to five minutes to attune a person.

As discussed earlier, an attunement is at the very core of Reiki therapy. The process of attunement is very precise and can be effected only by a Reiki master who has received an intensive training in the method. It comprises a series of four 'initiations' in which the master, using an ancient technology, transmits an amplified energy to the upper four chakras of the participant. This creates an open channel for cosmic energy to flow in through the top of the subject's head, through his upper chakras and out through his hands for use in future-treatments. During the entire ritual the participant is requested to remain calm and quiet and to keep his eyes closed.

"Why is there such secrecy about it? Why should I keep my eyes closed? What are you actually doing to me?" these are questions commonly asked by the participants and we find them quite understandable. No one can expect that a person would blindly permit to be subjected to a ritual that is likely to change his life. The answer to the above questions is quite simple. An attunement is a once-in-a-lifetime process during which extensive harmonization takes place within the subject's body. If he keeps his eyes closed and feels within himself, he can consciously participate in this unique event. Instead, if he follows the master's movements that are obscure for him in any case and constantly ponders on what effect this or that movement is likely to produce, he is least likely to perceive the fantastic changes taking place within him. It is, thus, in his own interests that the participant keeps his eyes closed. Again, the Reiki master can work with a greater peace of mind and concentration if two (or more) curious eyes are not intently gazing at him.

After the completion of attunements, the invigorated participants are requested to move back to the seminar-hall and resume (from where they had left) the laying on of their hands on their own bodies As they do so, they are immediately able to discern the difference in the energy-flow through their hands. Before the attunement, the flow was feeble, almost imperceptible; now, after the attunement, it is undeniably strong. This session of self-treatment continues till all the basic hand-positions have been covered.

The next session is devoted to treating others. Each participant is assigned a suitable partner and the two agree to exchange Reiki. Each person gives a full-body Reiki therapy to his partner and, in turn, receives the same from him. If time permits, the participants may also carry out a group Reiki session. It is here that a participant begins to feel the differences in energy drawn by different body-parts of an individual and differences in energy drawn by different individuals.

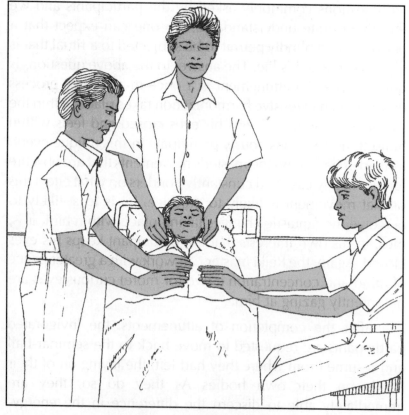

Fig. 4.1 : Group Reiki therapy

Many teachers suggest that each of the specified body-parts be treated for three minutes. While this is a good idea to begin with, we would suggest that you later follow the powers of your intuition and perception. Continue to treat a body-part till it draws energy. The moment it stops drawing energy, move to the next body-part.

With their bodies invigorated and minds opened up by Reiki, participants are, by now, quite relaxed and cheerful. Even those who are shy/reserved and who usually have closed personalities open up. Everyone feels being a part of one big, loving and lively family. Participants feel they have been friends for years. Indeed, many deep, lasting friendships are actually formed during the first degree seminar.

In the next session, the teacher gives guidelines for practice during the next few weeks (called the cleansing period). He also gives guidelines for treating common ailments using Reiki. He reaffirms the importance of chakras in treatment, reminding the participants of the body-region each chakra controls. The five spiritual principles of Reiki are, then, discussed at length, the teacher emphasizing that the mind and the body are intimately correlated.

At the end is an informal session where participants express their experiences. Each participant tells the class about what he felt while he was being attuned, while he was treating himself or his partner and while he was receiving treatment from his partner. The master clears doubts and answers questions raised by the participants. Finally, he thanks the participants for having attended the seminar and awards them the coveted certificates.

In conclusion, we will say that the first degree seminar is a milestone, in fact a turning point, in a person's life. The vibratory frequencies of his chakras are raised so that they become 'tuned' to that of Reiki. This tuning triggers a never– ending process of physical cleansing and spiritual evolution, literally transforming the person's life. There are no failed attunements as long as they are carried out by a trained master who performs the steps in a precise manner, making use of powerful symbols. This may sound a bit preposterous to your ears. After all, everyone makes mistakes and a Reiki master cannot be an exception. However, the point to be realised is that it is not the master who really brings about attunement. He only acts as a bridge between the universal life energy and the subject's bio-energy; the tuning is effected from 'above'.

The things that human beings do may be faulty or transitory. But a bond created by God is not subject to laws of the material world!

5. TREATING THE SELF AND OTHERS

The three-week period following attunement is a very important period in the concerned person's life as unprecedented physical, mental and spiritual changes take place in him. He is literally transformed into a new person : more healthy, more happy and more evolved.

This transformation is the natural outcome of a process of internal cleansing and detoxification that is sparked off by the attunement and which continues unabated as the person regularly channelizes Reiki while treating himself and others. Toxins that have accumulated in the physical as well as the energy-body for years, literally begin to be liberated and washed away by the floods of Reiki that invade the newly opened nadis (channels) within the body.

This process of detoxification can be further facilitated by –

(a) consuming a lot of pure water and fruit-juices,

(b) performing yogic breathing exercises (pranayam),

(c) eating lots of fruits, raw vegetables and sprouts, which provide us with vitamins and fibres,

(d) taking thorough, brisk baths at least once everyday,

(e) following simple Naturopathic procedures like steam-bath*, hot foot-bath*, whole body wet-pack*, etc.

While the body is busy eliminating toxins, it would, quite obviously, be undesirable to consume non-vegetarian foods, eggs, tobacco, alcohol and caffeinated beverages.

---

* Details of these simple procedures have been given in the book 'Nature cure for common diseases' by the same authors.

The process of detoxification may, initially, cause physical symptoms like running nose, diarrhoea, excessive sweating/urination, skin eruptions and mild fever. Symptoms of old disease (that had been suppressed by unwise medication) may reappear (albeit in a much milder form). All this time, however, the mind feels more and more better. Negative emotions like fear, anger, worries and apathy gradually disappear, giving place to positive emotions like confidence, peace, love, compassion and reverence for life. The person becomes self-reliant and capable of handling day-to-day problems with a 'never-before' ease. Old, bad habits are cast off. Stimulants lose their value in life. Gradually, a life-style develops, which is balanced, inwardly as well as outwardly. Some Reiki therapists have reported an unexpected development of extra-sensory powers (ESP) following regular use of Reiki.

It must have become quite clear to you, dear reader, that to derive the above-mentioned benefits to the maximum possible extent, it is necessary to channelize Reiki as frequently as possible by treating yourself (at least once every day) and others (your dear ones). The more you treat yourself (and others), the faster will your chakras spin, the more potent your nadis (channels) will become and the stronger will be the outward flow of energy through your palms. Then, the beneficial effects of your treatment will become more certain and consistent.

This chapter will give you complete details about Reiki therapy : rules to be remembered, precautions to be taken, body-parts to be worked upon while treating yourself and others. One word of caution : Do not, on your own, bring about any change in your medication. It is true that Reiki therapy brings about profound harmonization within the body and demonstrable physiological changes. Therefore, the doses of medicines you are taking will need suitable modification. However, you should entrust this responsibility to your physician.

Self-treatment

The best time for self-treatment is either early morning (as soon as you wake up from sleep) or late evening (when you are about to sleep). If the time necessary to accomplish full-body treatment is not available at a stretch, you can break-up the treatment into two (or more) parts, to be taken up at different times of the day. You might as well treat yourself while watching television, conversing with you family members or travelling.

Before you start treating yourself—
(a) remove shoes and loosen tight clothes/belts,
(b) wash your hands thoroughly with soap and water,
(c) briskly rub you palms against each other for a few seconds and bring your awareness to your palms. This will sensitise your palms and make you capable of perceiving the subtle energy-flow through your hands, as you sequentially place them on your various body-parts.

You are now ready to treat and invigorate yourself with Reiki. Switch off your door-bell, your pager/cell-phone; take your phone off the hook; request your family-members not to disturb you during the next few minutes. Lie or sit down as per your desire. Completely relax your muscles; let them go limp and slack. Slow down the rate of your breathing. Invoke Reiki, thanking it for accepting you as a channel. The various hand-positions for self-treatment have been depicted on the next few pages.* Lightly place your palms on each of these body-parts for about three minutes. If touching a body-part is impractical due to a boil, a wound or burns, palms may as

---

* The number and the nature of hand-positions vary slightly from healer to healer. The basic principle is : Cover as much body-area as practically possible.

well be held an inch or two away from the body. It is necessary to hold the palm slightly cupped and the fingers touching each other. Remember : scattered fingers mean scattered energy!

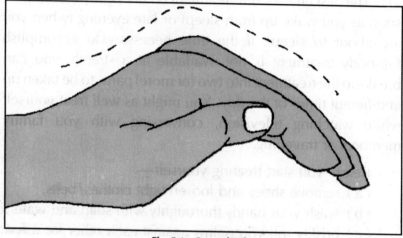

Fig. 5.1 : Cupped palm

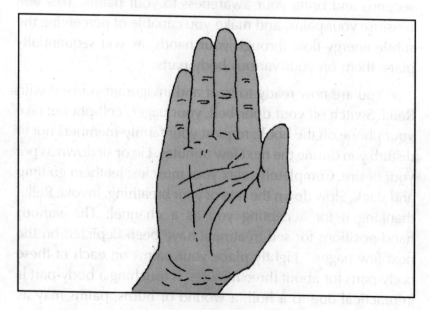

Fig. 5.2 : Fingers touching each other

Position 1

Objective : To provide Reiki to the crown (Sahasraar; सहस्रार) chakra, which governs the functioning of the fore-brain (cerebrum) and the pineal gland.

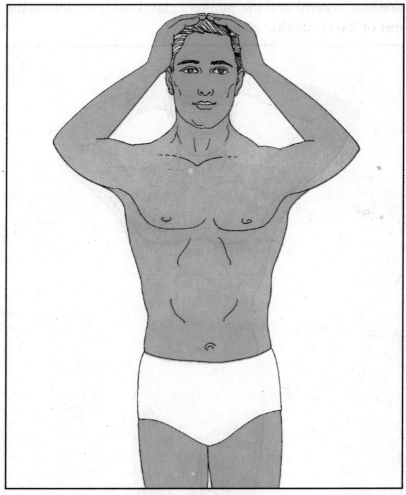

Fig. 5.3

Note : While you lay you hand on position 1, you may mentally chant the mantra aum (ॐ).

Position 2

Objective : To provide Reiki to the third eye (Aagyaa; आज्ञा) chakra, which governs the functioning of the cerebrum, the hypothalamus (which is the seat of the autonomous nervous system) and the pituitary gland (which controls the rest of the endocrine glands).

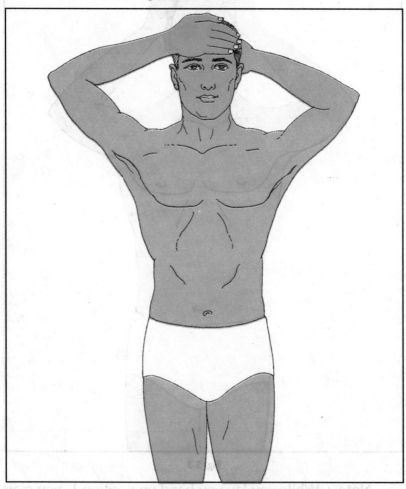

Fig. 5.4

Note : While you lay your hands on position 2, you may mentally chant the mantra am (अं) or ksham (क्षं).

Position 3

Objective : To provide Reiki to the eyes, the nose, the para-nasal sinuses and the mouth.

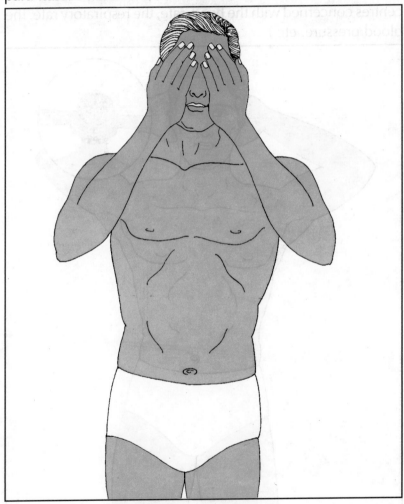

Fig. 5.5

Note : Avoid covering the nostrils.

Position 4

Objective : To provide Reiki to the ears, the hind-brain (cerebellum), the pons and the medulla (which contains vital centres concerned with the heart-rate, the respiratory rate, the blood pressure, etc.)

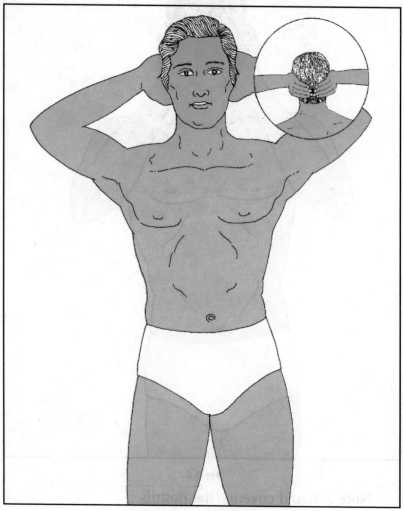

Fig. 5.6

Position 5

Objective : To provide Reiki to the throat (Vishuddha; विशुद्ध) chakra, which governs the functioning of the thyroid gland (concerned with the basal metabolic rate), the cervical nerve-plexus, the cervical vertebrae, the tonsils, the vocal cords and the food-pipe.

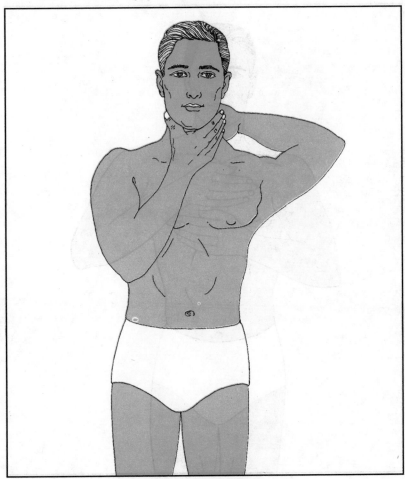

Fig. 5.7

Note : (a) The upper hand should be placed very lightly to prevent discomfort.

(b) You may mentally chant the mantra ham (हं), while you lay your hands on position 5.

Position 6

Objective : To provide Reiki to the heart (Anaahat; अनाहत) chakra, which governs the functioning of the thymus gland (concerned with our immunity), the brachial nerve-plexus, the arms, the heart and the lungs.

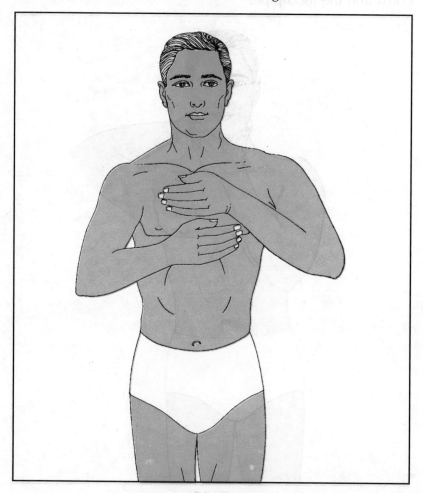

Fig. 5.8

Note : While you lay your hands on position 6, you may mentally chant the mantra yam (यं).

Position 7

Objective : To provide Reiki to the solar (Manipur; मणिपुर) chakra, which governs the functioning of the digestive organs (like the stomach and the intestines) and the accessory digestive organs like the liver and the pancreas (concerned with blood-sugar levels).

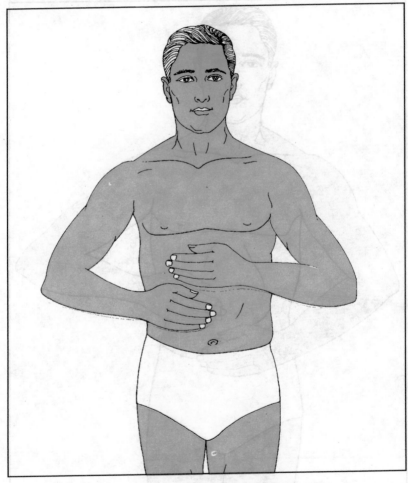

Fig. 5.9

Note : You may mentally chant the mantra ram (रं) while you lay your hands on position 7.

Position 8

Objective : To provide Reiki to the sacral (Swaadhisthaan; स्वाधिष्ठान) chakra, which governs the functioning of the reproductive system, the spleen (which is concerned with our immunity), the urinary bladder and the skin.

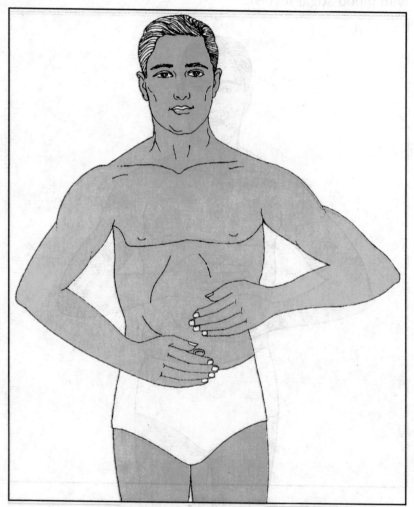

Fig. 5.10

Note : While you lay your hands on position 8, you may mentally chant the mantra vam (वं).

Position 9

Objective : To provide Reiki to the root (Moolaadhaar; मूलाधार) chakra, which governs the functioning of the adrenal glands, the urinary system, the external genital organs, the musculo-skeletal system, the hips and the legs.

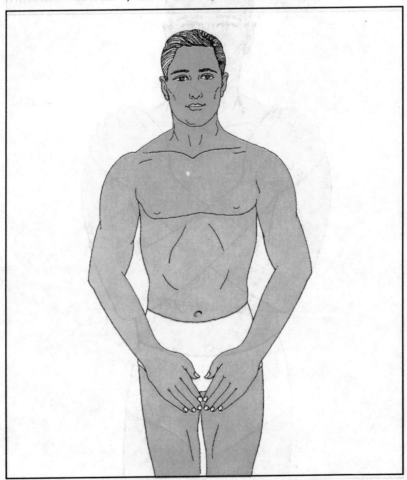

Fig. 5.11

Note : You may mentally chant the mantra lam (लं), while you lay your hands on position 9.

Position 10

Objective : To provide Reiki to the shoulder joints.

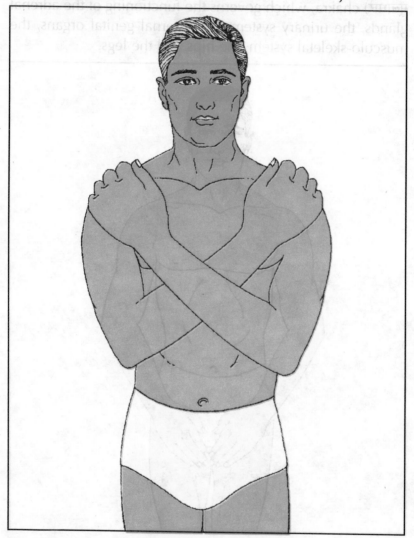

Fig. 5.12

Note : Some experts advise against keeping the arms/legs crossed while treating one's self. If you are not facing a shortage of time, you may as well treat one shoulder at a time, thereby avoiding the crossing of forearms.

Position 11
Objective : To provide Reiki to the elbow joints.

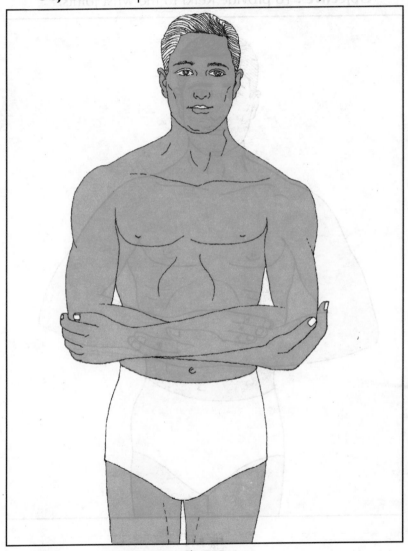

Fig. 5.13

Note : Some experts advise against keeping the arms/legs crossed while treating one's self. If you are having adequate time, you may as well treat first one elbow and then the other, thereby avoiding the crossing of forearms.

Position 12

Objective : To provide Reiki to the wrist joints.

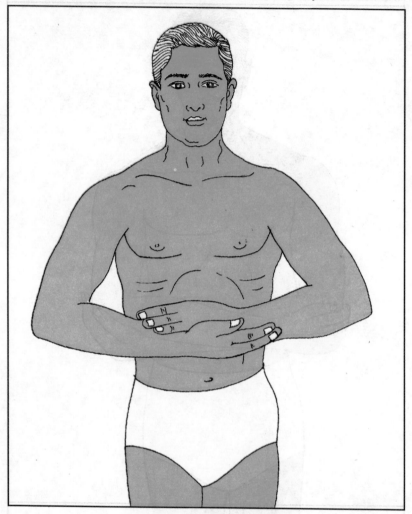

Fig. 5.14

Position 13

Objective : To provide Reiki to the knee joints.

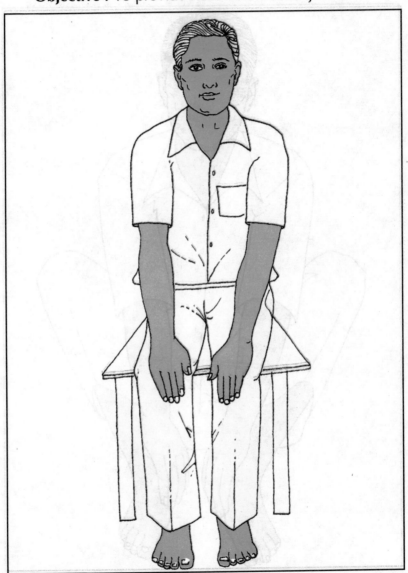

Fig. 5.15

Note : It is more convenient to be seated while laying hands on the knees.

Position 14

Objective : To provide Reiki to the ankle joints.

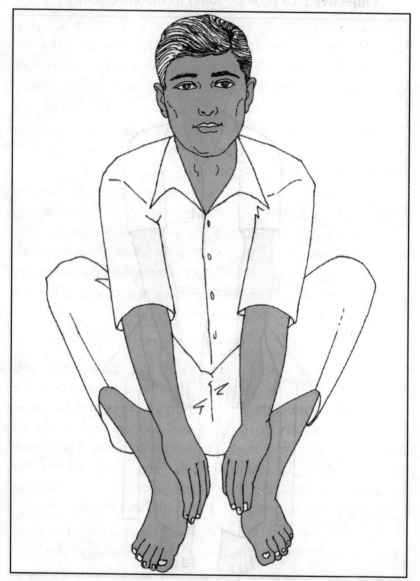

Fig. 5.16

Note : It is more convenient to remain seated while you lay hands on your ankles.

Further, you may lay your hands on the diseased part of the body if it has not, already, been covered by the standard 14 positions. Otherwise, completion of position 14 heralds the end of a full-body Reiki therapy session. Thank Reiki again for having come to your help. You must have realized that we have refrained from advising you to lay your hands on your back as it is quite uncomfortable, tiring the arms and tensing the muscles.

You may treat the diseased part of the body and the associated chakra for a longer time (say five to fifteen minutes) to derive greater and faster benefits.

It is quite obvious, that 'whole body Reiki therapy' is likely to take almost 40 to 45 minutes. On an exceptionally busy day, if you have less time at your disposal, you may stop a self-treatment session after you have covered the first nine body-positions. In case of an acute shortage of time, an injury or an emergency, you may treat only the diseased/injured body-part and the associated chakra.

Treating others

It has been stated earlier that the more Reiki you channelize, the more open your channels become and the more strong turns out the flow of energy from your palms. It is, therefore, necessary to treat others, too, as and when an opportunity presents itself. Whereas treating your own family-members is an easy job, requiring no further considerations, treating others (outsiders) is a somewhat different task, requiring a lot of thought and finesse.

(a) Wear clean, decent clothes. You may as well wear an apron to denote that you belong to the healing profession.

(b) Use no scents, perfumes or after-shaves as these may excite an allergic reaction in your patient.

(c) Introduce yourself and Reiki to the patient. Clearly tell him what Reiki can do and what it cannot, specifying that it is not a substitute for conventional medical treatment (rather it can be used in conjunction with medicines). Also state that you are only a medium through which Reiki will work. On the basis of this preliminary discussion, if you feel that you have not been able to establish a rapport with the patient, politely refuse to treat him. It is not your responsibility to heal everybody or the world! Again, avoid treating accident-victims. Such an unfortunate person will require scientific first-aid and quick hospitalisation. However, if your preliminary discussion with the patient has been congenial, decide to treat him and seek his permission. This is very important. Reiki therapy should be given only to an open person, who is ready to receive it; it cannot be forced upon someone. When treating an infant, a young child, an unconscious or an insane person, seek and obtain the permission of his close relatives.

(d) Inform the patient and/or his relatives about the remuneration you expect to receive against the time/services you offer. Never give away Reiki, as that makes beggars of people who receive it. Remember, though, that the exchange may be in forms other than monetary returns.

(e) Inquire into the patient's problems, with a view to understanding his disease well. However, do not venture to give a name or a label to the disease. Diagnosing the disease, in any case, is unnecessary for you, as you will be providing Reiki to his whole body.

(f) Request the patient to loosen tight belts/clothes.

(g) Wash your hands thoroughly with soap and water.

(h) It is neither desirable nor necessary to disrobe the patient while treating him. Clothes do not hinder the passage of Reiki into the body. In fact, Reiki can even pass through thick plaster-casts. This point has been raised over here to reassure such people who have had the misfortune of going through Reiki-books which depict nude figures, and who therefore, have come to entertain doubts about the sanctity of this therapy.

(i) Make the patient sit or lie down, as per mutual convenience. Do not allow him to cross his legs as that impedes free flow of energy.

(j) Invoke Reiki, mentally requesting it to help the patient, using you as a medium.

(k) Next, perform a procedure which is traditionally known as aura-sweeping or aura-smoothening. The objective behind this procedure is to render the patient's aura harmonius and more receptive to Reiki therapy. Keeping a distance of about two inches from the patient's skin, move

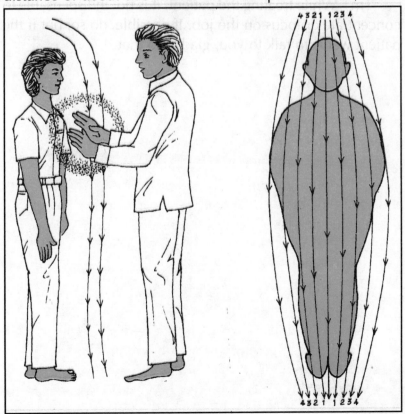

Fig. 5.17 : Aura-sweeping

your hands lengthwise along his body from his head towards
the toes, as depicted by line 1 of figure 5.3. Similarly, move
your hands from above downwards to trace paths 2, 3, 4 and
so on, as shown in the figure.

(l) You are now ready to give Reiki therapy to your
patient. Lay your hands gently for about three minutes on
each of the body-positions shown on the next few pages. If
touching a body-part is not quite possible (because it has a
boil, a wound, an ulcer or burns), hold the palms an inch or
two away. Remember to hold the fingers together and the
palms slightly cupped. Holding fingers apart results into a
scattering of energy.

(m) While treating the patient, it is not indispensable to
concentrate or focus on the job. If possible, do so; but if the
patient wants to talk to you, gladly do that.

Position 1

Objective : To provide Reiki to the crown (Sahasraar; सहस्रार) chakra, which governs the functioning of the fore-brain (cerebrum) and the pineal gland.

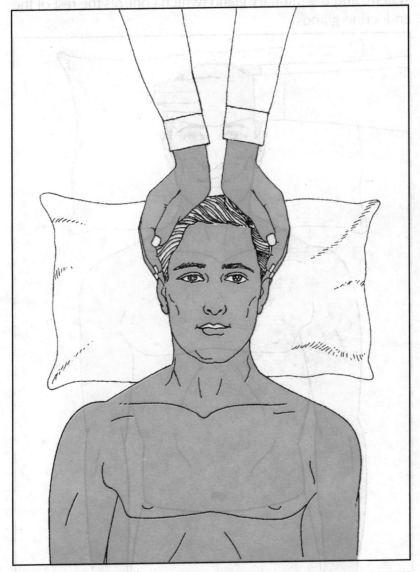

Fig. 5.18

Position 2

Objective : To provide Reiki to the third eye (Aagyaa; आज्ञा) chakra, which governs the functioning of the cerebrum, the hypothalamus (which is the seat of autonomous nervous system) and the pituitary gland (which controls the rest of the endocrine glands).

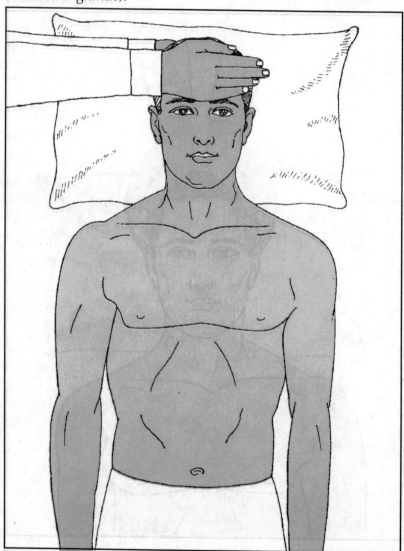

Fig. 5.19

Position 3

Objective : To provide Reiki to the eyes, the nose, the para-nasal sinuses and the mouth.

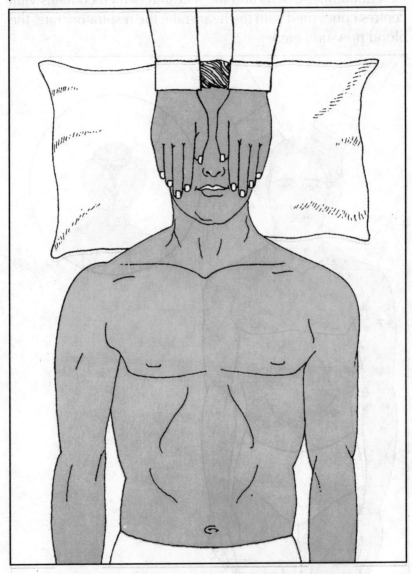

Fig. 5.20

Notes : Place the palms very lightly. Avoid covering the nostrils to allow free breathing.

Position 4

Objective : To provide Reiki to the ears, the hind-brain (cerebellum), the pons and the medulla (which contains vital centres concerned with the heart-rate, the respiratory rate, the blood pressure, etc.)

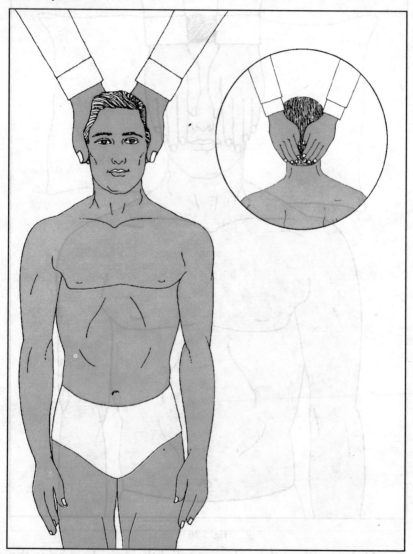

Fig. 5.21

Position 5

Objective : To provide Reiki to the throat (Vishuddha; विशुद्ध) chakra, which governs the functioning of the thyroid gland (concerned with the basal metabolic rate), the cervical nerve-plexus, the cervical vertebrae, the tonsils, the voice-box and the food-pipe.

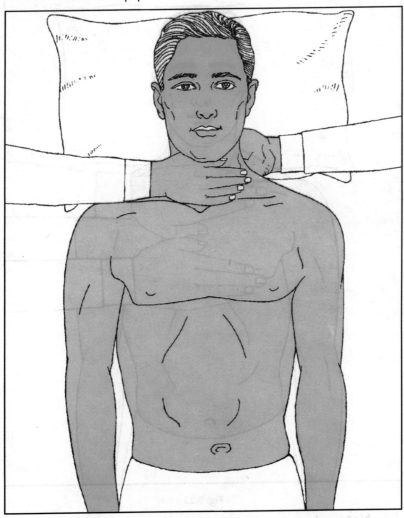

Fig. 5.22

Note : The patient may experience a feeling of choking if you place your upper hand too heavily.

Position 6

Objective : To provide Reiki to the heart (Anaahat; अनाहत) chakra, which governs the functioning of the thymus gland (concerned with our immunity), the brachial nerve-plexus, the arms, the heart and the lungs.

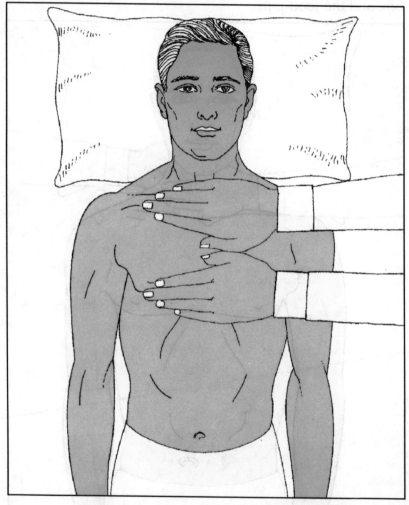

Fig. 5.23

Note : In case your patient is a lady, avoid actual contact of the body (the breasts); instead, hold your palms an inch or two away from the body.

Position 7

Objective : To provide Reiki to the solar (Manipur; मणिपुर) chakra, which governs the functioning of digestive organs (like the stomach and the intestines) and the accessory digestive organs like the liver and the pancreas (concerned with blood-sugar levels).

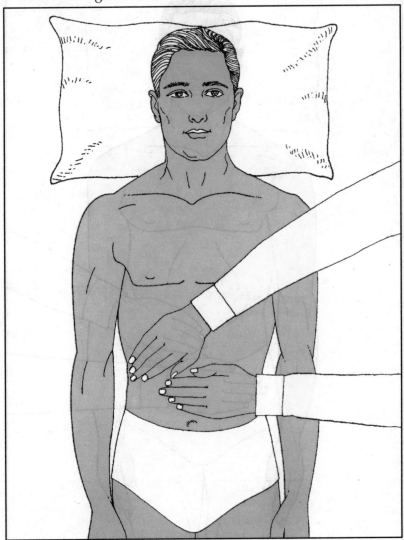

Fig. 5.24

Position 8

Objective : To provide Reiki to the sacral (Swaadhisthaan; स्वाधिष्ठान) chakra, which governs the functioning of the reproductive system, the spleen (concerned with our immunity) and the skin.

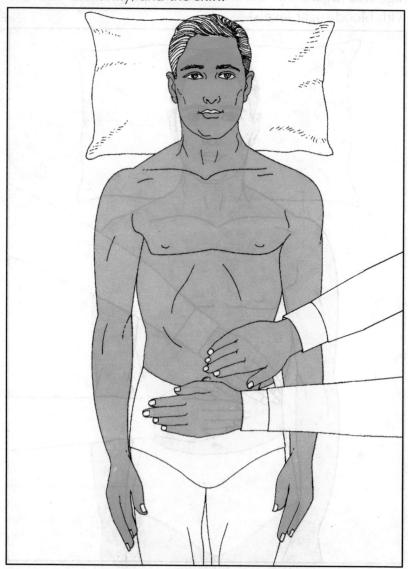

Fig. 5.25

Position 9

Objective : To provide Reiki to the root (Moolaadhaar; मूलाधार) chakra, which governs the functioning of the urinary system, the musculo-skeletal system, the legs, the external genital organs and the hips.

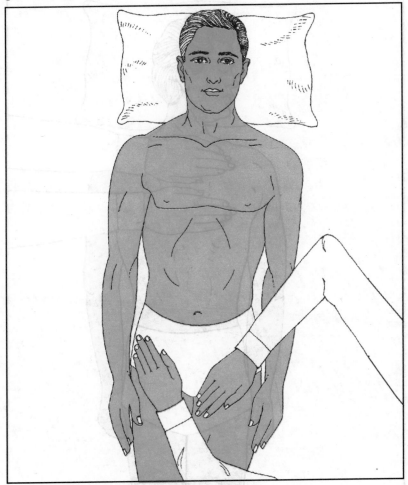

Fig. 5.26

Note : Avoid touching the body; hold your palms an inch or two away.

If the patient was, so far, lying on his back, now request him to turn around and lie on his stomach.

Position 10

Objective : To provide Reiki to the upper back which contains the thoracic vertebrae, as also the back-parts of the throat (Vishuddha) and the heart (Anaahat) chakras.

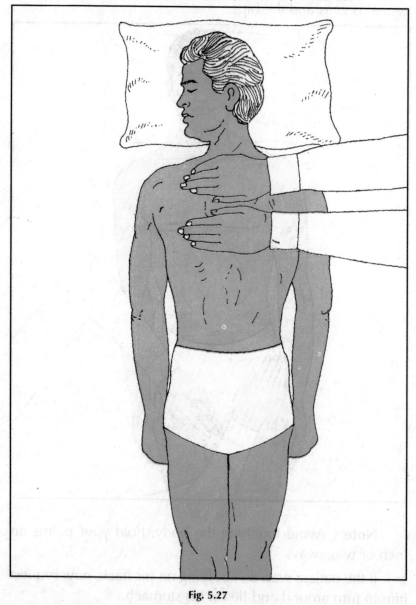

Fig. 5.27

Position 11

Objective : To provide Reiki to the middle back which contains the lumbar vertebrae as also the kidneys and the back-parts of the solar (Manipur) and the sacral (Swaadhisthaan) chakras.

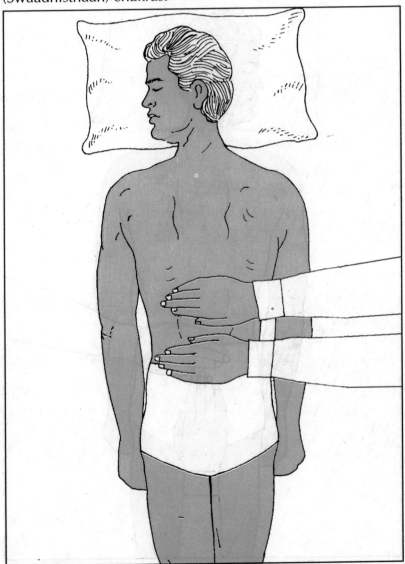

Fig. 5.28

Position 12

Objective : To provide Reiki to the lower back which contains the sacrum, as also the anus and the root (Moolaadhaar) chakra.

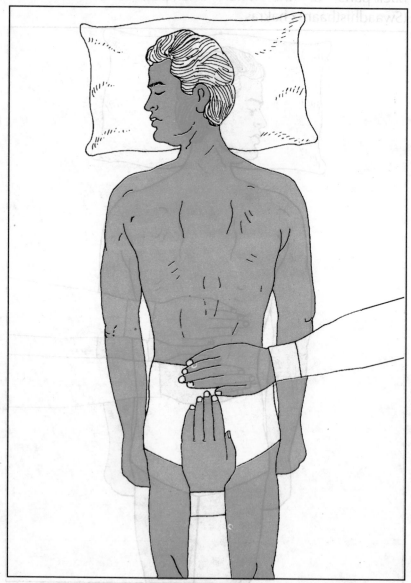

Fig. 5.29

Position 13
Objective : To provide Reiki to the shoulder joints.

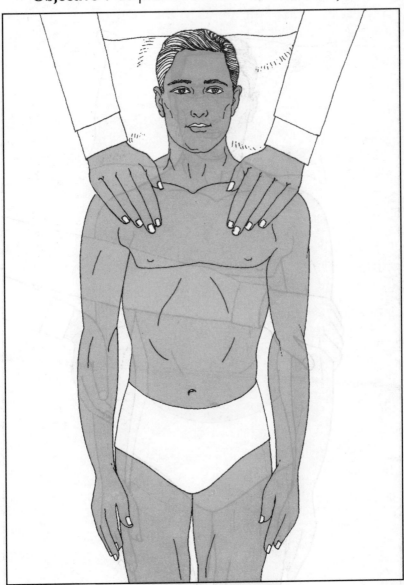

Fig. 5.30

Position 14
Objective : To provide Reiki to the elbow joints.

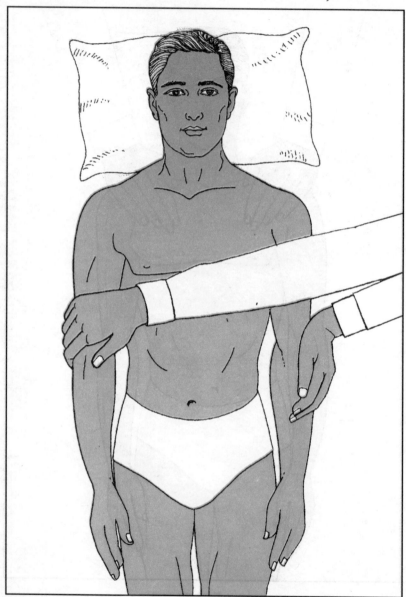

Fig. 5.31

Position 15
Objective : To provide Reiki to the wrist joints.

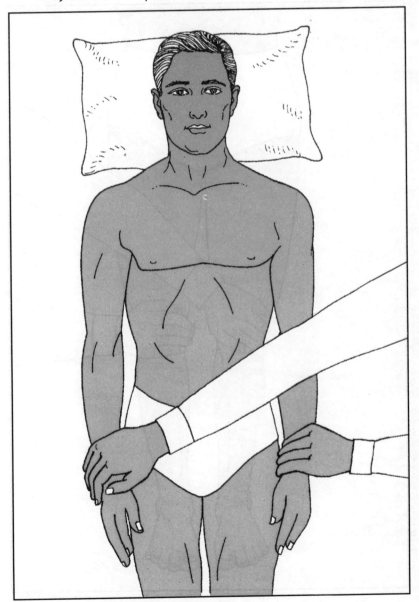

Fig. 5.32

Position 16
Objective : To provide Reiki to the knee joints.

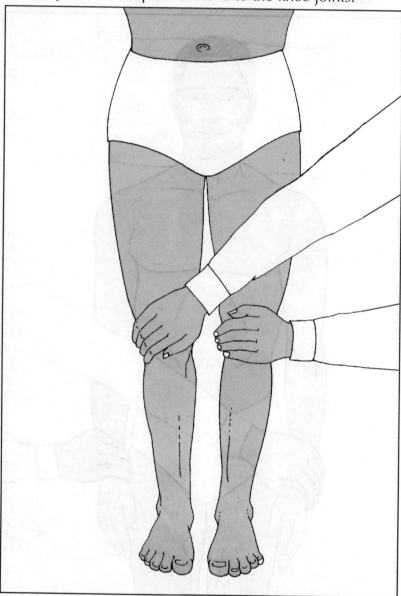

Fig. 5.33

Position 17
Objective : To provide Reiki to the ankle joints.

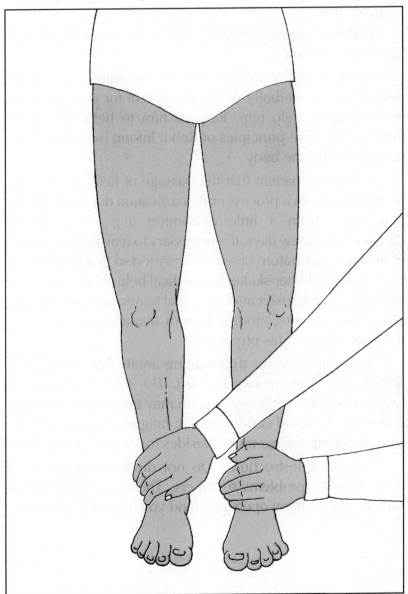

Fig. 5.34

Further, you may lay your hands on the diseased part of the body if it has not, already, been covered by the standard 17 positions.

Perform aura-sweeping again to smoothen and harmonize the aura.

Mentally thank Reiki again for accepting you as its instrument and verbally thank the patient for giving you an opportunity to help him. Request him to help himself by following the five principles of Reiki. Inform him about how the mind rules the body.

Inform the patient that the passage of Reiki through his body will initiate a process of detoxification due to which he may suffer from a little discomfort (e.g., fever, colds, diarrhoea) for a few days. It is necessary to reassure the patient of the transitory nature of such discomfort so that he does not panic and run helter-skelter for medical help. Also inform him that following detoxification, internal harmonization will take place, necessitating modification of medicinal doses under the supervision of his physician.

It is quite obvious that treating another person takes a little longer than treating the self. The total duration of a 'whole body Reiki therapy' session may turn out to be almost one hour. To avoid causing undue fatigue to yourself, make suitable sitting arrangements besides (or around) the patient.

One final instruction : Do not disclose the details of your patient's problems to others. These are 'professional secrets'; laying them open may land you into legal problems.

6. THE SECOND DEGREE TRAINING

The second degree Reiki seminar is aimed at bringing about a tremendous increase in your capacities as a healer. Things you only read in fantasy novels or objectives that seem incredible to logical ears become achievable through powers endowed by the second degree. This degree is a major tool of transformation for those who have decided to follow the path of spiritual growth.

While the curiosity about the second degree is aroused by the Reiki master's (seemingly incredible) comments at the close of a first degree seminar, the actual registration for the seminar is often sparked off by an amazing Reiki experience (e.g., recovery of a patient from a so-called incurable disease).

Much alike the first degree seminar, the second degree seminar, too, is designed differently by different masters. While the basic format remains the same, the presentation varies from master to master. Even a particular master may bring about spontaneous changes in the seminar, taking into account the level of the participants.

Before the proceedings begin, the teacher encourages each participant to describe the experiences he has had with the first degree. Any questions or doubts he has, as regards the first degree, are answered or cleared at this juncture.

The actual seminar begins with an initiation, which further attunes and energizes the chakras (especially the third eye or the Aagyaa chakra), fully opens up the channels and firmly anchors certain activated symbols in the participant's aura (so that they can be put to therapeutic use later).

Once all the participants have received attunements, the second session begins. Participants are informed about the three symbols that have been put into their auras. The rest of the second session is spent by the students in learning (by heart) how to draw each of these symbols precisely.

The third session is devoted to the understanding and learning of the use of these symbols. In essence, each of these symbols (especially 'hon sha ze sho nen') is sort of a focussing device which converts the divergent energy-waves into parallel ones.

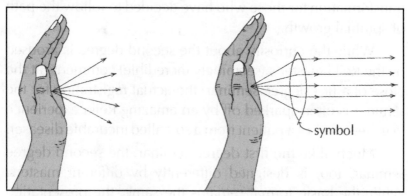

Fig. 6.1 : Energy emerging from the hands of a first degree holder is divergent.

Fig. 6.2 : Energy emerging from the hands of a second degree holder is rendered parallel by symbols.

Energy in the form of parallel waves is not only strong but can travel long distances without losing its punch. Unaided Reiki and symbol-aided Reiki can be compared to ordinary light and LASER, respectively.

The first symbol 'cho ku rei' is a 'power-symbol' in a literal sense. Its use increases the intensity of emergent Reiki manifold. In consequence, the duration of a treatment session comes down drastically. This is a big gain for Reiki therapists since most of them face severe constraints of time. In fact, it is this lack of time which prevents therapists from putting Reiki to as much use as they would like. The drastic reduction of treatment-period is also to the patients' advantage. Their time is not less valuable than that of the therapist.

The second symbol 'sei he ki' is traditionally called the mental healing symbol as it helps the mind and the emotions tremendously. The mind rules the body. Most diseases are, presently, considered psycho-somatic. Sei he ki heals the mind, thereby healing the body. When Reiki therapists use this symbol, they strike at the root of disease.

A regular use of 'sei he ki' results into an increased intuitive awareness. In the days following the second degree seminar, some participants develop extra-sensory powers (ESP) in the form of clairvoyance, clairaudience and clairsentience.

The third symbol 'hon sha ze sho nen' is the distance-healing (or absentee healing) symbol. It can be used to treat a person who is not physically present with you because (say) he is lying on a hospital bed or living in another town/country. When the healer imagines/visualizes the person requiring treatment and uses 'hon sha ze sho nen', an invisible bridge is formed between his Anaahat (heart) chakra and that of the patient. Reiki, then, flows along this bridge to reach the patient and brings about healing. Quite obviously, boundaries of space are suspended when this symbol is put to use. The therapist is no longer dependent on the proximity of a person to provide him Reiki. Does that sound incredible or implausible to you? If so, ask someone who has completed the second degree course to do distance energy transmission on you. Then you will know the truth for yourself.

We will like to add here that distance healing too, like hands-on healing, is to be given only on asking. Despite your good intentions (and the patient's ignorance), it cannot be forced on someone. In other words, you should obtain an express consent from the patient (or his relatives) before you start treating him.

In conclusion, we will say that the second degree seminar brings in its wake, a number of new possibilities and avenues of treatment for the participant. The attunement effected in the first degree is further strengthened and consolidated. Everything that you could do with the first degree can be done more quickly and intensely with the second degree. Moreover, it empowers you to heal the mind (which enjoys a complete reign on the body) and heal people living in any corner of the earth. In fact, you may join hands with other Reiki therapists to heal the whole world!

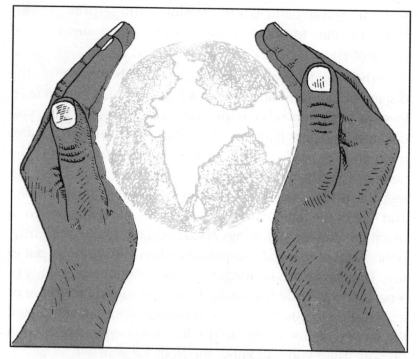

Fig. 6.3 : Making Reiki available to the world

7. THE THIRD DEGREE TRAINING

The third degree training is the most exciting part of the Usui method of natural healing. This is the teaching degree where you learn how to attune (the energy-bodies of) others and how to organise Reiki-seminars. In other words, the third degree training converts you into a Reiki-master. It also transforms you into a new person : more loving, more compassionate, more humble.

There is a great deal of discussion in traditional and modern Reiki-circles as to who are (or are not) the right candidates for the third degree training.

In traditional thinking, the master degree should be awarded only to a person willing to dedicate his life (and a fortune!) to Reiki. Again, the third degree training should not be given for the asking but should be offered by the teacher only to a deserving student. A deserving student is the one who, for many years, has been practising Reiki therapy, distance healing and mental healing to the satisfaction of the teacher. In other words, traditional Reiki masters accept only a select few students for the third degree training. They refuse to give this third degree training to students who do not fit into their criteria or do not meet their critical standards.

In our opinion, the master degree cannot be restricted only to those people who can dedicate their lives to the cause of Reiki. The world does not work that way any longer. Few people can really spend valuable years of their lives working as apprentices to Reiki masters and then pay huge amounts to receive the third degree training. The fact is that there is too much of ill-health and misery in the world. The earth is in pain. There is a real and urgent need of therapists who, working individually and unitedly, can heal this planet. And to create more healers, more teachers (masters) are desperately required. It would be immoral in these times to keep any healing system, especially Reiki therapy, exclusive. Any person who does so will be doing a great disservice to Reiki and will prevent it from becoming universal again as it once was. This view is endorsed by a number of modern Reiki masters.

We believe that any person who has mental integrity, who has treated numerous patients (by physical as well as distance transmission of energy) and who has a keen desire to teach Reiki therapy (i. e., to convert laymen into channels through the means of attunements) should be given a chance to undergo third degree training.

The third degree training cannot be imparted in a seminar. It is strictly a one to one proposition. In the first part of the training, the student receives the third degree attunement and is given complete information about one (or sometimes two) more symbols. Then, he is taught the steps to effect the first degree attunement. Next, he assists the master in conducting a couple of first degree seminars. At the end of this first part of training, he independently conducts a few first degree seminars.

In the second part of the training, the student is taught the steps to effect the second degree attunement. Next, he assists the master in conducting a couple of second degree seminars. At the end, he independently conducts a few second degree seminars.

In the final part of the training, the student is taught the steps to effect the third degree attunement. The moment he masters the procedure, the training ends. The student has now become a master himself.

In conclusion, we will say that the third degree training is the teachers' training program, after completing which you can attune the uninitiated. Purists say that 'If you are ready to give up everything to take Reiki into the world, you are ready to become a Reiki master'. We say that you need an intense desire to teach Reiki therapy to embark upon the third degree training. Do not join the third degree program thinking you will become a better or a more powerful healer (as happened after the second degree seminar). Rather, the third degree is about dropping your desire and need for power, about dropping your ego to realize that you are Reiki itself!

8. QUESTIONS AND ANSWERS

Q. 1. I have attended a first degree Reiki-seminar and have had my energy-body attuned. Yet, I do not feel a flow of energy through my palms. Why ?

Ans. 'Not feeling anything in the hands' is a common problem which some holders of the first degree face.

No feeling at all, while treating either the self or the others can only be attributed to a lack of perceptibility or sensitiveness (kinesthetic sense). The present age is that of competition and struggle for survival. This struggle, coupled with the flood of loud audio-visual stimuli that attack us each day, benumb our perceptive powers and render our hands insensitive to the subtle changes that occur when Reiki starts or stops flowing.

Do not lose heart. Continue treating yourself as well as others. As you relax your muscles, quieten your mind and focus on your hands, sensations will make themselves felt. This is as certain as the fact that day follows night. Your confidence will receive a further boost as people you treat give you a positive feedback.

Q. 2. I have been practising Reiki therapy for many months. At times I do not feel a flow of energy through my hands. Why ?

Ans. If the flow of energy is not felt occasionally, it is likely that the flow is actually not taking place. As you know, Reiki is drawn by the recipient rather than being given by you. If your patient does not require any energy or unconsciously blocks it, there may be no flow and you may not sense anything. One method of overcoming such a block to the inflow of energy has been discussed in Q. 13.

Q. 3. Does the same quality and quantity of Reiki flow through all hands (channels)?

Ans. While the quality is absolutely the same, the quantity of Reiki transmitted differs from therapist to therapist depending upon –

(a) how often he treats himself and others, since the channels become more and more potent (open) as they are increasingly put to use and

(b) how many degrees (of attunement) he has undergone, each further degree increasing his capacity to transmit energy many-folds.

Again, second and third degree holders use certain symbols which act as focussing devices, that render (the otherwise divergent) waves of energy parallel and, therefore, more penetrating.

Q. 4. Does Reiki flow only if I first offer prayers and then smoothen the aura?

Ans. Reiki always flows when needed and accepted by the recipient. There are no other pre-conditions. It is a God-intended or Nature-intended gift with no strings attached.

A prayer helps to quieten the mind which can, then, be focussed on hands, so that the subtle sensations (flow of energy) can be more easily felt.

Aura-smoothening is a dispensable procedure which strives to render the patient's energy-body more receptive to Reiki.

Q. 5. Do I myself need to have faith in Reiki to be able to help others?

Ans. No, Reiki is automatically transmitted if it is needed and accepted by the recipient. The energy flows and helps even if the channel does not believe it will work. Does a radio-set need to have faith in the B. B. C. (or any other station) to be able to reproduce the news being broadcasted by the B. B. C.?

Q. 6. Does the recipient need to have faith in Reiki to be benefited?

Ans. No, not necessarily. Reiki helps the recipient, whether he believes in it or not.

Reiki helps infants, animals and even plants. It helps insane or unconscious people, too. Here, quite obviously, the question of belief or faith does not arise. In other words, Reiki therapy cannot be written off as faith-healing, auto-suggestion or a placebo-therapy.

However, one point needs to be understood. Though not believing in Reiki, the recipient should be open-minded, prepared to judge it on the basis of pure experience.

Q. 7. Can Reiki be employed to prevent illness?

Ans. Reiki is, indeed, an excellent means of prophylaxis. A disease first arises at the energy level, and can be visualised (as an unevenness of aura) on a Kirlian photograph. If treated at this juncture, we can prevent the disease from striking the physical body. A regular practice of Reiki is, thus, almost a certain way of maintaining good health.

Q. 8. Should I always treat the whole body? Will it not be enough if I treat the diseased part alone?

Ans. If you have severe constraints of time, or if it is an emergency, you may as well treat the diseased part alone. A 'little Reiki' is certainly better than 'no Reiki'. Better still would be to provide Reiki also to the chakra that controls the diseased body-part.

However, our body is an indivisible unit, each body-part, each chakra intimately connected with the others. If sufficient time is available, it would be wiser to treat the whole body. That amounts to what is known as 'holistic healing'.

Q. 9. Is it possible to cure every type of health disorder by Reiki therapy? Can I give an assurance or a guarantee to the patient about the successful outcome of treatment?

Ans. Reiki therapy is not a 'cure-all' or a panacea. It can do a lot but it cannot do everything. In cases where pathological tissue-changes have reached a stage of no-return or in purely surgical cases (like mature cataract, hernia, heart valvular defects, etc.), Reiki may only be able to alleviate distressing symptoms.

Reiki therapy does not render conventional treatment superfluous. In fact, it can supplement and complement the latter.

Not even a high-charging surgeon gives an assurance about the successful outcome of the operation he is going to perform. Why, then, should a Reiki therapist do so?

Q. 10. How long (in terms of days) should I continue to treat a patient?

Ans. A patient with an acute disease should receive a minimum of three treatments, if possible on three successive days. The first treatment dislodges toxins from his body. The second treatment helps the body to flush these toxins out. Finally, the third treatment fills up the (purified) body with invigorating and rejuvenating energy.

Of course, if the disease has been present for many months or years, treatment may have to be continued for a long time before lasting benefits or improvement can be experienced by the patient.

The total duration of treatment cannot be predicted since no two patients, even though suffering from the same disease, respond in the same way to any particular mode of treatment.

Q. 11. Why is it that Reiki, sometimes, does not seem to work (help)?

Ans. Reiki therapists are aware of the fact that the results they expect do not always occur.

Reiki has its own wisdom and intelligence. It does that which is good for the recipient, rather than follow our wishes. The recipient as well as the therapist may desire a particular result (say relief from back-pain) but if there is some more pressing health-need (say relief from chest-congestion), Reiki will accomplish the latter first.

There are some other interesting reasons why Reiki fails to help.

To some people, Reiki therapy seems too very simple to be of help. They have never seen or encountered energy-healing earlier and would only be satisfied with something more 'solid' than Reiki. They are more likely to be helped by material modes of treatment like medicines, injections, surgery and so on. Different people are at different stages of (spiritual) development and they would require different modes of treatment.

In some people who come for treatment, the desire to be healed is simply an alibi. In their very core, such patients, consciously or unconsciously, do not want to regain health. They cling to their illnesses which are advantageous to them in some way. An illness allows us much-needed rest. It also gets us attention and sympathy. It brings our dear ones back to us. Seen from this perspective, falling ill is, actually, quite sensible!

A last category of 'problem patients' are those who are self-professed guardians of science. They come for treatment to prove that a method like Reiki therapy cannot possibly have any effect whatsoever. Full of scepticism and arrogance, they fight tooth and nail to prevent any flow of energy into their bodies.

In conclusion, we will advise you not to be disappointed if your expectations are not immediately fulfilled. With Reiki, nothing is achieved by pure will-power. Reiki channels are only media, not actual healers. They should remain neutral observers or witnesses of events. It is Reiki which works and it does that which is the best for the recipient.

In an acute or very serious disease, if things don't seem to be going to the patient's satisfaction, you should advise him to seek competent medical care.

Q. 12. I treat myself everyday with Reiki. Should I still pay attention to my diet and perform physical exercise regularly?

Ans. A well-balanced, cereal-centered, vegetarian diet and regular physical exercise are indispensable for maintaining/regaining good health. Reiki therapy does not allow a person to take undue liberties with diet. A diabetic who goes on eating sweets or a heart-patient who consumes a high-fat diet cannot hope to improve despite taking or receiving Reiki therapy religiously.

Q. 13. If Reiki is wise and intelligent and always flows when required, why do Reiki therapists use or promote crystals, scents, etc.? Is Reiki incomplete without such external aids?

Ans. Reiki does not require any external aid to be of help. However, in this materialistic world, many people like Reiki to be 'gift-wrapped' with crystals and/or scents.

It cannot be denied that crystals can first imbibe(store) any energy and, then, emit it in an amplified form for a long period of time.

A Reiki therapist can charge (say) a quartz crystal with Reiki by simply holding it between the palms for three to five minutes, requesting Reiki to purify and empower it.

Because of time-constraints, a Reiki therapist cannot remain with a patient for too long. He can give a charged crystal to the patient, to be kept in contact of the diseased body-part so that the latter can continue to receive Reiki even after an actual 'hands-on' healing session is over. For a therapist, a crystal is, thus, a time-saving device. For a patient, it is something which expedites recovery.

The property of a crystal to transmit Reiki in an 'amplified' form can be utilised to overcome energy-blocks in a patient's body. During treatment, if a particular body-part does not seem to be drawing energy (i. e., continues to feel cold to touch), a block may be suspected. A charged crystal may, then, be placed in contact of that body-part to demolish the block.

There are people who like to carry Reiki-charged crystals in there pockets or wear them on their bodies so as to receive the protective and health-giving Reiki round the clock.

In conclusion, we will say that crystals are quite useful for a first-degree practitioner whose energy-channels are still in the process of opening up and, therefore, the Reiki emerging from their hands is relatively feeble. For a second-degree practitioner, crystals are dispensable since he can intensify the energy-flow through his hands with the help of Reiki-symbols.

Scents, fragrances and essential oils used in Aroma therapy possess vital energies of flowers and herbs. These energies can be utilised to reinforce Reiki during attunement and/or treatment.

Q. 14. Can Reiki be put to uses other than human healing?

Ans. Alleviating human suffering is just one of the many uses Reiki can be put to.

Reiki can be used to treat animals, birds and plants, too. Animals simply love this healing touch. Seeds influenced by Reiki germinate earlier than ordinary ones. Plants that receive Reiki regularly grow much taller and stronger, and bear more leaves, flowers and fruits.

Fig. 8.1 : Energising animals   Fig. 8.2 : Energising plants

That Reiki can positively affect animals and plants is a proof to the fact that Reiki-healing is not the result of faith, suggestion or hypnosis.

Reiki can also be used to charge the food you eat. After a meal, you can lay your hands on your abdomen to provide Reiki to your stomach, thereby ensuring good digestion.

You can use Reiki to charge inanimate objects, too. You can positively charge your residence, your car, your office with this health-promoting energy. Your personal belongings like Jewellery, gem-stones, clothes, etc. can also be charged with Reiki.

Finally, you can charge your torch-cells or your car-battery with Reiki to keep them going for an incredibly long time.

APPENDIX 1
Reiki Research

Acceptable scientific research on Reiki is limited. However, even these few experiments compel us to accept Reiki as a potent therapeutic tool.

Effects of Reiki on human in-vivo haemoglobin and haematocrit values (oxygen-carrying capacity of blood) have been measured by Wendy Wetzel at the Sonoma State University. Blood samples of participants were drawn just before and immediately after a first degree seminar, and analysed. It was quite evident that everyone's haemoglobin and haematocrit levels showed statistically significant changes (rise). It was realized that the positive factors in the blood (e.g., haemoglobin) had increased, whereas the negative factors in the blood (e.g., cholesterol) had decreased. Such results go to prove the fact that Reiki is a balancing or harmonizing energy.

Effects of Reiki on blood pressure have also been determined. In the control group, there were no changes in anyone's blood pressure : measurements which were high/low in the beginning remained high/low and measurements which were normal remained normal. In Reiki classes, everyone with normal blood pressure continued to give normal readings. Participants with high/low blood pressure found that their blood pressure had been normalized. This experiment proves again that Reiki restores homoeostasis (the state of internal balance).

In 1987, Dr Janet Quinn reported a significant improvement in the immune function (CD 4 to CD 8 ratio) of subjects receiving therapeutic touch. It is for this reason that Reiki helps people with lowered immunity.

Dr Doniel Win of California demonstrated rapid and increased wound healing in student-volunteers who were given five minutes of touch-healing following surgical incisions.

At the McGill University in Montreal, Canada, Dr. Bernard Grad demonstrated that wounds of laboratory mice that received healing touch healed much faster than wounds of control mice. He also found that plants which received healing touch grew faster and stronger and produced more chlorophyll than control plants. Such experiments prove the fact that the benefits of Reiki are certainly not the results of belief or autosuggestion.

The fact that Reiki therapy or Reiki training brings about profound changes (for the better) in the subject's aura can be easily proved by Kirlian photography.

APPENDIX 2
The Chakras

Chakra	Name	Location	Physical counterparts	Organs controlled
	Sahasraar or Crown chakra	Top of the head	Pineal gland	Pineal gland, cerebrum, right eye
	Aagyaa, or Third eye or Brow chakra	Between the eye-brows	Pituitary gland; Cavernous or nasociliary plexus	Pituitary gland, hypothalamus (A.N.S.), left eye, ears, nose
	Vishuddha or Throat chakra	Base of the throat	Thyroid gland; Cervical or pharyngeal plexus	Thyroid and parathyroid glands, tonsils, voice-box, food-pipe, neck, mouth, tongue, arms
	Anaahat or Heart chakra	Centre of the chest	Thymus gland; brachial and cardiac plexuses	Thymus gland, the immune system, heart, lungs, the circulatory system, arms
	Manipur or Solar plexus chakra	Upper abdomen	Pancreas gland; Solar or coeliac plexus	Pancreas, the digestive system, liver, diaphragm
	Swaadhis-thaan or Sacral or Hara or Sexual chakra	Sacral region (below navel)	Gonads (testes and ovaries); Sacral or hypogas-tric plexus	The reproductive system, the urinary system, skin
	Moolaa-dhaar or Root chakra	Base of the spine	Adrenal glands; Coccygeal or pelvic plexus	Adrenal glands, the urinary system, external genital organs, musculo-skeletal system, legs

N.B. : The endocrine glands and the nerve plexuses have been further described in the next appendix.

APPENDIX 3

Endocrine Glands and Nerve-plexuses, the Physical Counterparts of Chakras

Two systems primarily govern the activities of the physical body : the endocrine system and the nervous system.

The Endocrine System

The system of endocrine glands controls the internal environment of the body. The endocrine glands are also called ductless glands because the secretions (hormones) they produce do not leave the gland through a duct but pass directly from the gland-cells into the blood stream.

The endocrine system comprises of 1 pituitary gland, 1 pineal gland, 1 thyroid gland, 4 para thyroid glands, 1 thymus gland, 2 adrenal or supra-renal glands, numerous (pancreatic) islets of Langerhans and 2 sex glands (i.e., ovaries in females or testes in males).

The pineal gland is situated in the brain. While its physical functions are not clearly known, it is believed that the pineal is concerned with our intuitive and extra-sensory powers. The pineal receives its energy from the Sahasraar chakra.

The pituitary is called the master endocrine gland because it governs the activities of all other endocrine glands. It secretes a number of hormones viz. TSH (which controls the thyroid), ACTH (which controls the adrenals), LH+FSH (which control the ovaries and the testes) and growth hormone (which controls the growth of the body). A deficiency of growth hormone results in retarded physical growth. The pituitary receives its energy from the Aagyaa chakra.

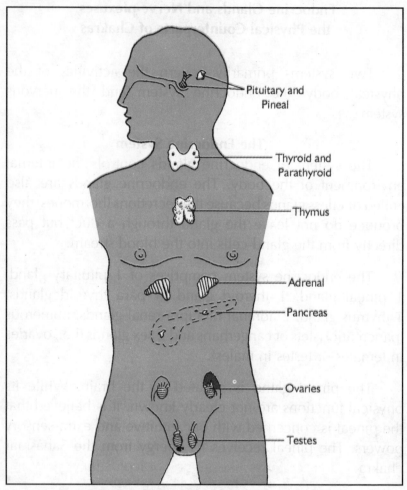

The endocrine glands

The thyroid is a 'H' or butterfly shaped gland situated at the base of the neck, overlying the voice-box. It produces hormones like thyroxine and tri-iodo-thyronine which are concerned with the body's heat (basal metabolic rate). Moreover, these hormones are necessary for our mental and physical development and for the health of our skin, hair and nerves.

Disorders of the thyroid include (a) underactivity or hypothyroidism and (b) overactivity or hyperthyroidism. Their symptoms have been tabulated below :

	Hypothyroidism	Hyperthyroidism
1	Incidence equal in both sexes	More common in females
2	Metabolic rate is slow	Metabolic rate is fast
3	Body is cool	Body is hot, due to which there is excessive sweating
4	Tendency to gain weight in spite of meagre diet	Tendency to lose weight in spite of increased appetite
5	Blood pressure is low and pulse is slow	Blood pressure is high and pulse is rapid (always above 100/min)
6	Physical and mental lethargy (slowness)	Physical overactivity with trembling (esp. of the fingers) and nervous tension

The parathyroids are four very small glands which lie just behind the thyroid. They secrete parathormone which is necessary for the metabolism of calcium in the body.

The thyroid and the parathyroid glands receive their energy from the Vishuddha chakra.

The thymus gland lies in the upper chest, in front of the heart. It produces thymosin which stimulates immunity. The thymus receives its energy from the Anaahat chakra.

The adrenal glands lie above the kidneys. They produce a number of hormones like gluco-corticoids (necessary for glucose-metabolism), mineralo-corticoids (necessary for electrolyte balance), sex hormones (oestrogen in females and androgens in males) and stress hormones (adrenaline and nor-adrenaline, which help us to cope with acute stress). The adrenal glands receive their energy from the Moolaadhaar chakra.

The islets of Langerhans in the pancreas produce two hormones : insulin and glucagon. While insulin strives to reduce the blood-glucose level, glucagon tries to raise it.

A controlled secretion of these two hormones results into balanced levels of glucose in the blood.

Each cell of our body requires glucose for its surivval. Insulin pumps glucose present in the blood into the cells. In the absence of insulin, glucose cannot enter the cells and, therefore, accumulates in the blood causing diabetes. Uncontrolled diabetes produces three classical symptoms : excessive hunger, excessive thirst and excessive urine. Other common symptoms of diabetes include recurrent boils, failure of wounds to heal, frequent changes in spectacle-glass numbers and itching about the genitals. The pancreas receives its energy from the Manipur chakra.

The ovaries produce oestrogen and progesterone. The testes produce testosterone. These sex glands receive their energy from the Swaadhisthaan chakra.

The nerve-plexuses

The nervous system can be divided into the central nervous system (which comprises the brain, the spinal cord and peripheral nerves) and the autonomous nervous system.

There are 43 pairs of peripheral nerves of which 12 pairs (called cranial nerves) arise directly from the brain and the rest 31 pairs (called spinal nerves) arise from the spinal cord.

The spinal nerves are named and grouped according to the level of vertebral column from which they emerge :

8 cervical nerves (C_1 to C_8)
12 thoracic nerves (T_1 to T_{12})
5 lumbar nerves (L_1 to L_5)
5 sacral nerves (S_1 to S_5)
1 coccygeal nerve.

In the cervical, lumbar and sacral regions, the spinal nerves unite near their origins to form large masses or networks of nerves called plexuses. In each plexus, many nerves are regrouped and re-arranged before proceeding to supply the skin, muscles and joints of a particular area.

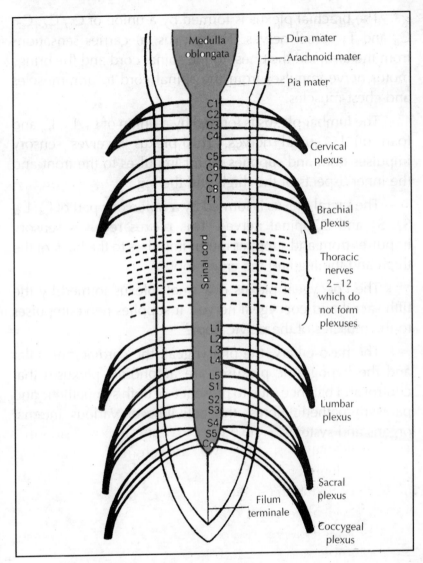

The nerve-plexuses

The cervical plexus is formed by a union of C_1, C_2, C_3 and C_4 spinal nerves. This plexus (a) carries sensations from the back of the head, the side of the head and the neck to the spinal cord and (b) brings motor nerve-impulses from the spinal cord to the neck-muscles and the diaphragm.

The brachial plexus is formed by a union of C_5, C_6, C_7, C_8 and T_1 spinal nerves. This plexus (a) carries sensations from the arm and the chest to the spinal cord and (b) brings motor nerve-impulses from the spinal cord to arm-muscles and chest-muscles.

The lumbar plexus is formed by a union of L_1, L_2, L_3 and (part of) L_4 spinal nerves. This plexus receives sensory impulses from and supplies motor impulses to the front and the inner aspects of the thigh and the leg.

The sacral plexus is formed by a union of a part of L_4, L_5, S_1, S_2 and S_3 spinal nerves. This plexus receives sensory impulses from and supplies motor impulses to the back of the thigh and the leg and the entire foot.

The coccygeal plexus is a small plexus formed by the fifth sacral and coccygeal nerves. It supplies nerve-impulses to the muscles of the pelvic floor.

The naso-ciliary, the pharyngeal, the cardiac, the solar and the hypogastric plexuses are autonomic plexuses that control and balance (due to presence of both sympathetic and parasym pathetic fibres) the activities of various internal organs and systems.

APPENDIX 4
Suggestions for Reiki Therapists

We have presented in this chapter, some practical suggestions and guidelines for practising Reiki therapists who have recently entered the field.

Many of the points mentioned here might be already known to you. However, we have presented them here with a view to reinforcing your knowledge. At the same time, we invite suggestions from you. They will help us to enrich our knowledge and to render future editions of this book more complete and useful.

(1) Be well conversant with the nature of Reiki and its place in the field of therapeutics. Procure knowledge about human anatomy, human physiology and human diseases (their symptoms and conventional treatment).

(2) Fully explain to the patient what Reiki therapy is and what it strives to achieve. Never say, 'It cures'. Say, 'It harmonizes the physical and the energy bodies.'

(3) Seek an 'express consent' of the patient and/or his close relative before treating him. Reiki therapy should only be given on asking and should not be forced onto somebody.

(4) Be particular about hygiene. Wash your hands before and after treating a patient.

(5) Hold your fingers gently together and the palm slightly cupped. Fingers held apart result into an unnecessary dispersion of energy.

(6) When doing 'hands-on' healing, place your hands lightly on the patient's body (i.e., avoid putting undue pressure on his body).

(7) In general, give full-body treatment irrespective of the nature of the disease. Only in case of an emergency or an acute shortage of time should you treat the diseased/injured part alone.

(8) Avoid the temptation to prescribe anything, to anybody, at any time. It is illegal for a person who is not a registered medical practitioner to prescribe a medicine. This includes vitamins, minerals, herbal medicines, tissue (Biochemic) salts and Homoeopathic medicines.

(9) Do not guarantee results. Remember that you are only acting as a medium (bridge) between the universal energy and the patient's bio-energy. It is just not possible to predict the rate of recovery because no two persons (even though suffering from the same disease) respond to Reiki therapy in the same way. Don't practise Reiki therapy in an indiscriminate manner. Be aware of its scope and limitations. It is irresponsible and unethical to raise false hopes. If you tarnish the image of Reiki therapy, good work of even ten Reiki-therapists may not be able to redeem it.

(10) Do not undertake to treat seriously ill patients. Serious diseases call for hospital-treatment. Reiki therapy is not a substitute for competent and urgent medical care.

Published by   Navneet Publications (India) Ltd., Dantali, Gujarat.
Printed by   Dila Printers, Ahmedabad. Tel. 2120123